Connected
Real Estate

**Essays from innovators
in real estate, design, and construction**

Edited by Kevin O'Donnell
and Wolfgang Wagener

The Cisco® Internet Business Solutions Group (IBSG), the global strategic consulting arm of Cisco, helps Global 500 companies and public organizations transform the way they do business—first by designing innovative business processes, and then by integrating advanced technologies into visionary roadmaps that improve customer experience and revenue growth.

The Cisco IBSG Connected Real Estate Practice provides trusted, independent advice to senior executives from some of the world's largest organizations. The highly experienced team develops real estate solutions, technologies, and systems for real estate and multi-industry sectors, helping to transform user experiences, streamline and enhance the design/build process, reduce building lifecycle costs, and foster environmental sustainability.

CISCO

Published by
Torworth Publishing
35 The Strand
Walmer
Kent CT14 7DX
United Kingdom

First published 2007

ISBN 978-0-9551959-1-4

A catalogue record for this book is available from the British Library

Edited by Kevin O'Donnell and Wolfgang Wagener

CONTENTS

Introduction: How technology transforms built environments
Kevin O'Donnell, Executive Consultant, Internet Business Solutions Group,
CISCO, UNITED KINGDOM
Dr. Wolfgang Wagener, Head of Real Estate Innovation, Worldwide
Real Estate and Workplace Resources Group, CISCO, UNITED STATES

INTRODUCTION

WE STAND ON THE CUSP of an exciting transformation of our physical environment.

Kevin O'Donnell
EXECUTIVE CONSULTANT, INTERNET BUSINESS SOLUTIONS GROUP
CISCO, UNITED KINGDOM

Dr. Wolfgang Wagener
HEAD OF REAL ESTATE INNOVATION, WORLDWIDE REAL ESTATE AND
WORKPLACE RESOURCES GROUP, CISCO, UNITED STATES

The editors would like to thank Mark Golan for his valuable contributions
in writing, structuring, and editing this introduction.

Mark Golan
VICE PRESIDENT AND WORLDWIDE LEAD, CONNECTED REAL ESTATE,
INTERNET BUSINESS SOLUTIONS GROUP, CISCO, UNITED STATES

How technology transforms built environments

THE POWER OF TECHNOLOGY to transform societies is a cornerstone of our history. In the last 150 years, scientific exploration and invention led to huge technology infrastructures that transformed built environments and the way we use them. Technology led to metropolitan, then national and international infrastructures for power, water, transportation, and communications. These advances added value to real estate by creating environments that liberated human activities from site and climate, intensified space use, and facilitated urban development.

IN THE 20TH CENTURY, new technologies in the form of the steel frame, curtain wall, elevator, electricity, and air conditioning led to buildings as we know them today. Here in the 21st century, digital technology continues to accelerate our ability to increase real estate values. Technology is again changing how we design and construct buildings and the building fabrics themselves: both how we operate and maintain them as well as how their occupants experience and use them.

The real estate, design, and construction industry is central to the well-being of the global economy. It contributes 10 percent to the worldwide GDP, employs more than 100 million people, and produces the places where we live, work, play, and learn.[1] For 2006 alone, the construction output is estimated at US$4.6 trillion for commercial, residential, and infrastructure construction, and renovation.[2]

We have chosen to conceptualize the impact of technology within real estate in the context of the transformations it enables.

1. Norbert W. Young Jr. and Harvey M. Bernstein, *Key Trends in the Construction Industry* (McGraw-Hill Construction, 2006).
2. Norbert W. Young Jr. and Harvey M. Bernstein, *Key Trends in the Construction Industry* (McGraw-Hill Construction, 2006).

3

An entirely new class of services is changing workplace environments, the use of space within buildings, and the development of entire communities. Today's technology is also modernizing building operations, design-build processes, and the environmental performance of buildings. Taken together, these real estate transformations will enhance user experiences, streamline design-build processes, reduce the cost of the building lifecycle, and foster environmental sustainability.

Transforming building infrastructure and services

The real estate, design, and construction industry has been exploring the concept of an intelligent building since the 1970s, when computer-driven technologies influenced office and building automation and were incorporated into the physical fabric of buildings. A good definition of an intelligent building was given by Arup, one of our book's contributors, as "one in which the building fabric, space, services, and information systems can respond in an efficient manner to the initial and changing demands of the owner, the occupier, and the environment."[3] Although this definition paints a vision, we need to explore how this will actually occur. What has kept this vision from being realized in the past and what has changed that makes it possible today? Put simply, the change has been digital technology.

Fully integrated communications become the foundation for as yet uninvented applications and services that transform the ways that we create and use the places where we live, work, play, and learn.

Technology is the transformational agent that enables this vision, and connectivity is the critical attribute it creates. In this context, connectivity can be thought of as the ability to facilitate interaction among devices and systems to enable new services. We can think of connectivity in buildings from two perspectives: the IT perspective and the building-systems perspective. In the IT world, convergence combines data, voice, and video onto a common network. This network becomes the fourth utility alongside water, electricity, and gas.

The real-estate perspective combines these IT elements with building-automation systems to form a single, digital infrastructure.

---

3. http://www.arup.com/communications/skill.cfm?pageid=4311.

Building-automation systems include heating, ventilation, and air conditioning (HVAC); lighting; physical security and access control; fire and life safety; elevator and electrical controls; digital signage; programmable surfaces and light-emitting diode facades; and smart sensors. It envisions connecting everything that merits control using one wire, one protocol, one data framework, and one application interface to enable solutions that lower cost and drive services aligned with the use of the property. The building can be thought of as the embodiment of the network—the physical framework in which it's deployed.

As the cost of adding a device drops and its value increases, additional devices will be added, mostly in the form of sensors. This will continue to enhance the value of all the devices pursuant to Metcalfe's Law, which states that the value of a network is proportional to the square of the number of devices on the system. Put another way, this means each device becomes more powerful as other devices are added to interface with it. For example, the value of a phone in a network of a million phones is much greater than the value of a phone in a network of just 10. Flexible, programmable event-correlation software—which triggers automated actions—will further enhance this value, while wireless mesh networks will make deploying sensors cheaper over time.

A good example of the role of event-correlation software involves energy use. Assume electric utilities move to a variable-pricing structure where rates are higher during peak usage periods and lower during periods of low demand (this appears likely to occur in many places). Event-correlation software could be used to raise the thermostat set point (assuming it's summer) and dim the lights automatically, based on a signal from the electric utility that indicates the system is entering a peak load period and, in response, raises rates for its duration. This software allows building operators to take humans out of the decision process by deploying predetermined, rule-based actions that lead to greater efficiency.

The process of adding cheap sensors will be enabled by using low-power, wireless means of connecting to the network. This saves money by eliminating the need to cable each device. This process will culminate with "dust" technologies that embed sensors directly into the materials of the building itself, allowing a building to monitor its own environment and structural health. In the end, buildings will become a collection of thousands—and possibly millions—of sensors, all interacting with each other and directing actions independent of human beings to improve the efficiency and performance of the building.

With this fully integrated digital infrastructure, building owners and operators can transform their properties and business models, differentiate themselves from competitors, and deliver innovative services at lower costs. Innovative services can be thought of in two categories: operational services that are common to all buildings, and industry-specific services for different building types. Operational services focus on elements common to all buildings, such as energy, comfort, and life/safety management. A fully integrated digital infrastructure can substantially streamline operational processes to reduce their cost, which can be as much as 80 percent of the cost of the entire building lifecycle.[4] Industry-specific services vary with the use of the building. These solutions start to become indistinguishable from those created from an IT perspective. They benefit, however, from the additional devices and sensors that can be brought to bear for a given solution.

An example of operational services can be seen in James J. Whalen's essay "Attaining Operational Excellence," which explains how Boston Properties centralized its IT network to streamline property operations, improve customer experience, and reduce operational expenses dramatically. A vision for operational services and new user experiences is described in "The Way Smart Buildings Will Flourish," by Dr. Ludger Hovestadt. He envisions buildings in 2020 where occupants access on-demand services through a personalized user interface. Dr. Sing Tien Foo provides an industry-specific example of how commercial real-estate operators can increase their cash flow and, therefore, asset values by broadening their business models to include new revenue-generating services enabled by technology in "Connected Singapore: Evolving from Landlord to Facilities Service Provider," where he describes the value creation in the Suntec City development.

Transforming workplaces

Digital technologies give us more options for designing and using our workplaces. In the corporate world, real estate is typically the second-largest business expense—about 5 percent to 10 percent of operational budgets—after human resources.[5] It is also the largest long-term asset on most company balance sheets. CoreNet Global, the leading association for corporate real estate and related professionals, says that

4. Panama Bartholomy, *Building Green in the Golden State* (California Conservation Corps., 2005).

5. Menhere and deJonge, *Kapitaal Verdeling* (Delft University, 1995).

6

up to 60 percent of assigned workspaces are wasted because people are in meetings, not at their desks.[6] This is a stunning statistic; it means that the majority of a company's largest asset class is unused. This most likely represents the largest area of waste remaining in corporations today. Even more important, a company's work environment is one of the largest determinants of culture and worker productivity. By better aligning the work environment with the needs of the worker, space is reduced while productivity is improved.

Organizations are moving from a mindset of "my space" to "team space." Resulting benefits include increased productivity, intensified space usage, and reduced environmental footprint.

In his essay "Architectural Consequences of Connectivity," William J. Mitchell discusses the dynamic nature of space and the obsolete value of space assignment. He offers insights for using space more efficiently, along with design considerations for collaborative office environments that support employees who may be engaged in a number of simultaneous tasks. Space will be transformed "on the fly" to suit the immediate needs of users, such as checking e-mail, attending a formal meeting, or participating in an informal whiteboard session. Programmable surfaces—such as whiteboards, walls, screens, or building exteriors—allow information to be created, shared, stored, and accessed through the use of digital media. In his essay "Justifying Place in a Virtual World," Dr. Frank Duffy focuses on a similar theme. He challenges organizations to embrace the "networked office," a new method of designing office space to address the realities of today's dynamic, mobile workforces.

In his essay, "Banking On Tomorrow's Workplace," Mark Nicholls explains the complex process of reshaping Bank of America's 90 million square feet of real estate into networked workplaces that meet both customer expectations and the economics of supporting today's flexible workforces.

In a world where many corporate environments have become nondedicated, organizations will have an opportunity to outsource a portion of the workplace to a "workplace service provider." In "Work

6. *Corporate Real Estate 2010 Survey* (CoreNet Global, 2005).

Without Boundaries," Mark Dixon addresses how companies can do this using a shared portfolio. By sharing environments with other companies, organizations can provide better services to their people while lowering costs and improving flexibility in the portion of the portfolio for which it's most required.

To enable the transformations discussed previously, the corporate real estate group must collaborate with the IT and human resources organizations to deliver work environments that support the achievement of business goals. Elements of these corporate functions have already become a single "work environment" function although organizational structures haven't yet changed to accommodate this reality. In "The Role of the Workplace in Achieving Strategic Business Goals," José-Ramón Burgos emphasizes the importance of this collaboration to effect change management. He also emphasizes the importance of distance collaboration in an increasingly global world, along with incorporation of technologies such as videoconferencing that enhance collaboration and effectiveness.

Transforming design-build processes

The U.S. Department of Commerce measured contract value in dollars per construction work hour and discovered that the productivity of the construction industry has steadily declined since the 1970s, contrary to productivity gains in all other nonfarm industries.[7] Studies by the construction industry agree that only 10 percent of labor and materials costs are value-added activities, with 30 percent administration and 60 percent waste.[8] This implies that more than US$2 trillion a year is wasted. This is greater than the GDP of all but five countries in the world. The lack of interoperability among computer-aided design, engineering, and other software systems in the construction industry alone costs US$60 billion each year. Owners and operators directly bear about two-thirds of this expense.[9]

Adopting digital Building Information Models can improve productivity and interoperability in the design and build processes,

---

7. Paul Teicholz, *Construction and Non-Farm Labor Productivity Index 1964–2003*, (U.S. Department of Commerce, 2004).

8. Construction Industry Institute, The University of Texas at Austin, 2004.

9. *Key Trends in the Construction Industry* (McGraw-Hill Construction, 2006).
   Based on Michael P Gallaher, Alan C. O'Connor, John L. Dettbarn, Jr., and Linda T. Gilday, *Cost Analysis of Inadequate Interoperability in the U.S. Capital Facilities Industry* (National Institute of Standards and Technology, 2004).

helping to eliminate this monumental waste. It can also yield significant building-lifecycle savings and create a higher-quality environment. One way it accomplishes this is by allowing us to create buildings "virtually," before starting construction. This strengthens today's fragmented construction industry by enabling vertical integration among the many participants involved in creating a building. At its heart, the Building Information Model has a massive, centralized database of knowledge and designs that all stakeholders can access. Instead of a linear flow of tasks and information, stakeholders can share their information to develop ideas and solve problems in parallel.

The Building Information Model is the technology platform that strengthens today's fragmented design and construction industry by enabling vertical integration among the many disciplines and participants in the creation of the built environment.

In "A Collaborative Model for the Construction Industry," Dr. Bernhard Bürklin discusses the fluid nature of the construction process and how the Building Information Model can accomplish what we've discussed previously. We anticipate that as architects, engineers, consultants, and construction companies discover the power of interconnected IT systems to improve their own productivity, they will become champions for integrating digital technology capabilities and services into the built environments they create. These professionals are just beginning to discover this potential, as described by A. Eugene Kohn and James R. Brogan in "Connectivity and Building Design." In "Performance-Based Design and Connected Practice," Terry Hill and Dr. Chris Luebkeman of Arup also describe how knowledge management and digital simulation tools can facilitate better design and best practices.

As the digital Building Information Model takes hold, we expect new ecosystems of partners to emerge that are better able to meet client demands. The detailed databases created during the design-build phases of the building lifecycle have additional value for the operations and maintenance phases. Handing off these databases to operational organizations provides a strong, real-time knowledge base for day-to-day operations. It also assists them with simulating user requirements.

Transforming environmental sustainability

Environmental sustainability is a major global trend for the 21st century. Investors are increasingly aware that environmental policies and regulations will affect shareholder value. Buildings account for half the world's energy consumption.[10] On average, digital infrastructure is the second-largest consumer of energy in buildings. The largest consumer is HVAC, much of which is spent to cool IT systems.[11] While IT systems are essential, strategic components of buildings, they are rarely factored into the environmental sustainability equation. Taking advantage of these systems provides many opportunities to improve sustainability, including reducing the resources needed in manufacturing and distribution, cutting the energy and materials consumed during operational lifecycles, improving health and productivity effects on users, and properly disposing of toxic electronic waste.

Buildings account for half of the world's energy consumption and generate far more greenhouse gas emissions than any other industry sector.

Dr. Volker Hartkopf and Vivian Loftness develop in "Strategies for Sustainable Built Environments" a vision for buildings that generate more energy than they consume. Carnegie Mellon University (CMU), led by the Center for Building Performance and Diagnostics (CBPD)—a National Science Foundation Industry/University Cooperative Research Center—is preparing to realize this vision with the Building as Power Plant (BAPP) project on the CMU campus.[12] BAPP seeks to integrate clean building technologies with innovative, distributed energy generation systems, so that all of the building's energy needs for heating, cooling, ventilating, lighting, and information technology are met on-site, maximizing the use of renewable energies. Connectivity and distributed sensing systems are crucial for the success of managing these clean building technologies to create energy effectiveness.

10. R. K. Stewart, FAIA, Facilitator of the AIA Sustainability Summit Task Force, American Institute of Architects (AIA), December 2005.

11. Cisco estimate based on sources from Arthur D. Little, 2002, and *Good Practice Guide* (U.K. Department of Environment, 1996), p118.

12. Carnegie Mellon University, http://www.arc.cmu.edu/bapp/index.html

The Bank of America essay in this book describes the bank's commitment to achieving platinum Leadership in Energy and Environmental Design (LEED) certification, the highest voluntary national standard for developing high-performance, sustainable buildings. When the 52-story Bank of America Tower at One Bryant Park, Manhattan opens in 2008, it will be the first high-rise office building in the world to attain the LEED platinum building standard.

Workplace design also has a direct effect on environmental sustainability. Redesigning workspaces can shrink the environmental footprint of organizations by reducing square footage per employee and, in turn, facility and IT expenditures. For example, in a 100,000-square-foot building, a 40 percent reduction in square footage per employee could save 1,500 tons of concrete, 280 tons of steel, and 2,850 tons of carbon dioxide emissions during construction—the equivalent of taking 560 passenger cars off the road for a year.[13]

Transforming communities

The year 2007 is a milestone in that, for the first time in history, more than half of the world's population now lives in cities.[14] The world's population is expected to reach 9.4 billion by 2050, and by then, more than 60 percent of the population will live in urban areas.[15] This growth is helping drive long-term demand for buildings and is forcing a re-evaluation of how to design communities. Whether the focus is a single building, a small group of buildings, or the creation of an entire city, our message remains relevant. For this book, we sought contributions from those responsible for large-scale real estate developments to test the relevance of citywide network connectivity for communication and collaboration to enhance urban design and management, simultaneously reducing carbon emissions.

New Songdo City is a metropolis under construction in South Korea, home to the world's most computer-savvy populace. In his essay "New Songdo City: Building Experiences, Interactions, and a New Way of Living," Stanley C. Gale shares his vision for a ubiquitous city and

13. Cisco estimate based on the following sources:
Davis Langdon, City of London Commercial Sector Cost Estimation, December 2004; www.greenhouse.gov.au/yourhome/technical/fs31.htm; the U.K. Grid Energy Emission factor of 0.469kgCO2/kwh; and www.usctcgateway.net/tool/.

14. *World Urbanization Prospects* (United Nations, 2004).

15. *World Urbanization Prospects* (United Nations, 2004).

reminds us that, "The goal is not to build wired buildings and cities, but to build inspirational buildings and cities in which technology enables personal lifestyle choices and corporate innovation."

Most of us don't have the advantage of creating a city from the ground up. How do we transform the thousands of cities we already have? In their essay "Milla Digital Zaragoza: a New-Century Public Realm," Juan-Alberto Belloch, José-Carlos Arnal, and Dennis Frenchman discuss the vision and challenges of transforming the 2,000-year-old city of Zaragoza, Spain with a new "digital mile" of media-rich public spaces designed to attract innovative people and investment. In the "Building Digital Beijing" essay, Zhu Yan relates the role of digital communications and media in the city's plans to host the 2008 Summer Olympic Games, creating a legacy that encourages learning and enhances the future prosperity of the city.

Reconfiguration of social and economic activities, due to emerging location freedoms, will result in a new distribution of familiar building types and urban patterns.

This book offers a series of essays by thought leaders throughout the real estate, design, and construction industry. It strives to present a well-rounded view of the trends toward Connected Real Estate with perspectives from owners, designers, builders, operators, corporate users, industry consultants, and influential academicians. We hope this book extends your understanding of the roles that built environments play in supporting the values and needs of your culture and society. We invite discussion and ideas as we partner in our efforts to realize the vision of Connected Real Estate.

KEVIN O'DONNELL & WOLFGANG WAGENER

MARK GOLAN

VICE PRESIDENT AND WORLDWIDE LEAD, CONNECTED REAL ESTATE
INTERNET BUSINESS SOLUTIONS GROUP, CISCO, UNITED STATES

Mark Golan is vice president of the Connected Real Estate Practice within the Cisco Internet Business Solutions Group. His team develops real estate solutions, technologies, and systems for real estate and multi-industry sectors, helping to transform user experiences, streamline and enhance the design/build process, reduce building lifecycle costs, and foster environmental sustainability.

During the past five years with Cisco, Golan served as vice president of Worldwide Real Estate and Workplace Resources, where he directed the company's global real estate portfolio and associated services. Prior to joining Cisco, he held senior finance and engineering operations positions with a small artificial intelligence company, Sun Microsystems, and Hewlett-Packard. He also spent a total of eight years with Smith Barney and Morgan Stanley in a variety of investment banking roles.

Golan is an active member of CoreNet Global, the leading association for corporate real estate and related professionals, where he currently serves as chairman. He also serves as a Cisco representative and board member for the Silicon Valley Chamber of Commerce, and is a member of the Board of Advisors for both Realcomm and the *Journal of Corporate Real Estate*.

Golan graduated with honors from Tufts University with a bachelor of arts degree in economics. He received a master's degree in business administration with distinction from The Amos Tuck School of Business Administration, Dartmouth College, where he was elected a Tuck Scholar.

KEVIN O'DONNELL

EXECUTIVE CONSULTANT, INTERNET BUSINESS SOLUTIONS GROUP,
CISCO, UNITED KINGDOM

Kevin O'Donnell, executive consultant for the Cisco Internet Business Solutions Group, consults with global organizations to help them develop innovative, flexible working environments.

In the last 20 years, O'Donnell has worked with Global Fortune 500 companies to develop solutions that address critical business problems. In recent years, he has focused on collaboration opportunities within the workplace so that companies can gain a competitive advantage. He has also developed a number of simulation models for analyzing scenarios to investigate potential outcomes associated with planned decisions.

Prior to joining Cisco, O'Donnell worked as a management consultant for Pricewaterhouse-Coopers, and as a lecturer at the University of Manchester, United Kingdom.

DR. WOLFGANG WAGENER

HEAD OF REAL ESTATE INNOVATION, WORLDWIDE REAL ESTATE AND
WORKPLACE RESOURCES GROUP, CISCO, UNITED STATES

Wolfgang Wagener came to Cisco with an international background in architecture, urban planning, and real estate development. His focus is on improving the business performance of private and public sector organizations through design solutions that deliver on the high potential of digital technology while elevating the quality of the built environment and employing environmentally sustainable practice.

Wagener, a member of both the American Institute of Architects (AIA) and the Royal Institute of British Architects (RIBA), practiced architecture with Murphy/Jahn Architects in Chicago and Richard Rogers Partnership in London. In Los Angeles, he led his own architecture and planning consulting practice serving private and public sector clients. He was a visiting professor at the architecture and urban planning schools at both the University of California, Los Angeles, and the University of Southern California. He has received grants from the European Union, the American

13

Institute of Architects, the Graham Foundation, and the National Endownment of the Arts. He is also the author of *Raphael Soriano* published by Phaidon Press.

Born in Essen, Germany, Wagener received a master's degree and doctorate in architecture and urban planning from Aachen University in Germany, and an advanced management degree in real estate from Harvard University.

1 TRANSFORMING BUILDINGS

Fully integrated communications become the foundation for, as yet, uninvented applications and services that transform the ways that we create and use the places where we live, work, play, and learn.

TO PROVIDE building owners and users with flexible, cost-effective and "green" environments we need better collaboration among all participants across the building lifecycle.

Dr. Bernhard Bürklin
HEAD OF CORPORATE DEVELOPMENT, HOCHTIEF, GERMANY

A collaborative model for the construction industry

THE CONSTRUCTION INDUSTRY IS FACING A SERIES OF FUNDAMENTAL CHALLENGES that is affecting every player in the building lifecycle, from architects to owners to tenants. Despite technology advances, the vast majority of buildings cannot be repurposed easily enough to meet the changing business needs of their occupants. Likewise, many owners continue to focus their attention on up-front construction costs, even though they are dwarfed by ongoing building-management costs that ultimately account for up to 75 per cent of the total outlay for the building during its lifetime. And despite a pressing need for innovation, tendering processes in some countries actually discourage new ideas and put further pressure on the wafer-thin margins that characterise the construction industry. The list goes on, and many of these challenges are not new. What is changing, however, is our willingness and ability to tackle them.

WE BELIEVE THREE FACTORS WILL BE CRITICAL to the evolution of the industry in the coming years. Firstly, there will be significant change in building design, which will alter the way we use and manage buildings. Secondly, we will develop new ways of constructing buildings, adopting better processes and sharing information more effectively in order to get closer to our goal of "repeatable uniqueness"—a way of standardising processes even as we recognise every building is different.

Most important, new collaborative relationships will be formed between all participants in the building lifecycle, breaking down the functional silos that characterise the industry today and enabling architects, engineers, construction companies, owners and tenants to work together more effectively. In turn, these changes will be supported by a range of technologies, including onsite, wireless applications;

visualisation technologies deployed at every phase of development, from design to facilities management; and embedded technologies that provide true plug-and-play flexibility.

Designing plug-and-play buildings

Architecture is rapidly evolving, with free-form buildings beginning to replace traditional, rectangular designs, and advanced, environmentally friendly materials more widely deployed. Yet at a more fundamental level, change is not happening quickly enough. Although buildings are inherently inflexible because of their physical constraints, it is still possible to offer a much more flexible environment for owners and tenants than we do today.

To begin with, the concept of plug-and-play should apply to all technologies within a building, from telephony and audiovisual to television. Tenants do not want to deal with networking and telephone cables, switches and routers, or connections to the Internet. They want to be able to plug into a data port and automatically be connected to the technologies they need, whether it is building services or their own proprietary data network. In other words, those technologies should become a standard service, in much the same way that electricity, water and gas are provided at the flick of a switch or the turn of a tap. If tenants know they can switch these services on and off easily, they can get up to speed faster when they move into a property, and have far greater flexibility when they want to repurpose or relocate.

Technologies should become a standard service, in much the same way that electricity, water and gas are provided at the flick of a switch or the turn of the tap.

These needs should be considered from the very beginning of the building lifecycle, so that the enabling components can be built into the core infrastructure. Ultimately, plug-and-play capability will extend beyond the building itself: it should be possible for tenants to plug into their "virtual office" regardless of where they are, whether using a cell phone, a PC or a voice-over-Internet telephone.

There is also a growing need for architects to work new capabilities into the building fabric to make building services easier to manage. Sensors are commonly used to monitor heating, ventilation and air conditioning—but they can also be used in numerous other applications. It is possible, for example, to monitor the flow of current to lighting fixtures, giving facilities managers advance warning when a light bulb is becoming inefficient. The more we can embed these kinds of capabilities into the initial design, the better operational environment we provide.

Over time, these design changes could have broad implications both for the industry and for building occupants. Theoretically, these modifications should generate a need for more research and development, which will help fuel interest in our sector within universities and industry and reverse the current decline in civil-engineering students. The construction industry, in particular, has a poor reputation among younger people, resulting in a drop in the number of university students specialising in civil engineering in many countries—which will lead to severe skills shortages in the medium term. More fundamentally, these design changes may encourage organisations to rethink the way they use buildings. If a plug-and-play environment makes it easy to get connected, regardless of location, companies may be tempted to work out of multiple, smaller offices rather than central headquarters, providing greater convenience for employees and allowing employers to seek out the best rental or ownership deals.

Challenges facing the construction sector

As the design sector addresses these fundamental issues, the construction industry too faces its own unique challenges. Firstly, the margins under which we operate are extremely tight —despite the high risks we take, many companies operate on margins as slim as 2 per cent. Secondly, and at the same time, we are under relentless pressure to build more quickly and more efficiently—our United States operation, Turner, recently completed a large turnkey project in just over three months.

While these factors would ordinarily trigger industry consolidation, the construction market remains determinedly fragmented and is likely to stay that way. In Germany, for example, the largest construction company has a market share of little more than 1 per cent, and the combined market share of the top 10 companies is far below 10 per cent. We have not seen a big trend toward contractors purchasing rivals to create supercontractors, nor has there been extensive consolidation among architects. In part, this is because the first stage of the lifecycle—design—is a more "artistic" activity than the process-oriented, scientific construction sector, and if you cannot make it process-oriented, you lose many of the benefits of consolidation. We believe that when consolidation does happen, it will more likely be between different parts of the building lifecycle rather than within them, similar to the way that both HOCHTIEF and Turner have expanded into facilities-management operations.

This has a number of implications. For starters, without consolidation there is less market pressure to drive efficiencies in the building lifecycle and push through change. Furthermore, it means that relatively few companies have the resources to research and drive the kind of change the industry needs. Cost, in fact, is the biggest inhibitor to innovation for all of us.

In addition, some fundamental characteristics of the construction market need to be radically changed. The European market, for example, urgently needs to adopt new tendering methods. At the moment, the tendering process in countries such as Germany— particularly in the public sector—is typically driven by the architect, and is based on submissions made in response to a functional description or a bill of quantity. The contractors are obliged to meet those requirements, and there is no scope for introducing different designs or different models. In fact, in the public sector there is often a legal disincentive to accept alternate designs, since contractors may complain that the tendering process did not create a level playing field. Because of this, competition in the tendering process focuses on price—further driving down margins and creating a hostile relationship between contractor and client—and innovation is stifled.

Achieving repeatable uniqueness

We are tackling challenges on two levels—by improving our own construction processes, and by improving collaboration between the different players in the overall building lifecycle. From a construction perspective, our goal is repeatable uniqueness. Looking beyond the basics of standardising safety checklists or project scheduling, repeatable uniqueness is about working out how we can take our best business disciplines and apply them universally. Some of these process changes will be fundamental. For example, we are increasingly moving toward a prefabricated building model, shifting more of the hardcore construction work from the site to our own production yards. The aim is to do the more difficult and dangerous work in factories where it can be regulated closely, and then carry out simpler assembly work on the production site. This moves the industry to a more efficient model, similar to the automotive industry, and also has significant, positive repercussions in terms of health and safety. There has been an irreversible trend toward improving safety at the sites over the past decade, and we have taken continuous steps to reduce accident rates.

From a construction perspective, our goal is repeatable uniqueness.

Similarly, we are weaving environmental ("green") construction techniques into our building processes. Environmental standards in Germany are very stringent, and energy efficiency, recycling, building-materials selection and waste control are relatively advanced compared to the United States. Historically this was partly driven by higher energy costs in Europe, but there are also political and social factors. As a company, however, we take a similar approach to green issues in the United States, where we now have some 40 green-certified buildings with different levels of platinum and gold certification. Turner did not wait for regulations to adopt these green practices; in many cases, it built them into its construction processes before the customer even asked for them.

Repeatable uniqueness is also about taking disciplines from one stage of the building process and using them elsewhere. For example, if we use radio frequency identification (RFID) technologies to track goods during the building process, could we not build similar technologies into the core infrastructure, so that facilities managers could use RFID for preventative and corrective maintenance?

While these changes may seem far-reaching, it is important to bear in mind that, as an industry, we have always been efficient at managing processes. When the new Commerzbank Tower was built in the centre of Frankfurt, many large components—some of them up to five metres wide—were preassembled off-site and had to be brought in by road. For several weeks, traffic in downtown Frankfurt was blocked off each evening, and all the traffic lights and signs were removed so that these huge columns could be brought in by road. Everything was then reassembled by early morning ahead of the next day's rush hour. This was a complex logistical exercise, repeated over and over again, and demonstrates just what the industry is capable of. Similarly, at HOCHTIEF we have proven how effectively we can collaborate internally.

We believe that technology will play a significant role in supporting this evolution within the construction sector. At a strategic level, technology supports our efforts to extend best-practice processes and provides a platform for information exchange and collaboration. At a tactical level, we are also adopting a number of specialist technologies, including four-dimensional modelling. These are three-dimensional models that add the dimension of showing construction-process evolution over time—where architects, owners, project participants and regulatory authorities can look at detailed building views together and consider alternative strategies.

At a strategic level, technology supports our efforts to extend best-practice processes and provides a platform for information exchange and collaboration.

One of the biggest challenges the construction industry faces is communications—not just the reach, but also in ensuring that accurate, up-to-date information is being distributed. Onsite, we use a wide range of technologies, some of them common but deployed in new ways. For example, our two prime methods of communications are e-mail and push-to-talk phones. But the true value of both comes when they are integrated with our operational systems, built into workflows so they become task-oriented, and applied as just-in-time learning tools. For example, safety checklists can be sent over the phone; alternatively, if I am onsite and have forgotten my safety training, I can access a short video or brief training document.

Wireless, of course, is a core technology, and we believe that it will underpin our efforts to create a "job-in-the-box." Our vision is to provision a site with a wireless infrastructure so we can be up and running immediately, rather than waiting for the last mile of the communications connection. We are also starting to use voice over Internet so that we can avoid bringing in local carriers, and can have people onsite acting as a virtual office with their own extension numbers.

A collaborative model for the building industry

As we work within the construction sector toward our goal of repeatable uniqueness, our second objective is to improve the level of collaboration between the different players in the building lifecycle.

The functional silos that characterise our industry—like so many others—are major impediments, and there is unrelenting pressure for architects, engineers, construction companies, owners and tenants to work together more effectively. The bottom line is that if we want to provide owners and tenants with flexible, cost-effective and green environments—and if we want to do so in a way that is profitable and efficient for all the participants in the lifecycle—we need better coordination among the participants.

In part, this requires a change of mind-set. Architects need to involve construction companies routinely during the design stages, which will allow us to advise on embedded technologies and discuss how green requirements will affect factors such as layout, usability, and so forth. There are already examples of this happening in the design of schools, where the use of the campus and facilities tends to be analysed in great detail. Likewise, owners need to take lifecycle management issues into account when they commission buildings. Instead of focusing all their attention on the up-front costs, there will be greater benefit if they address green issues and operational factors during the design phase, rather than later in the lifecycle. There will also be benefits to the tenant if owners spend more time assessing the facilities-management implications early, which will reduce operational overhead—and this may roll back to the owner in the form of enhanced tenant satisfaction and higher occupancy rates.

Our vision is to provision a site with a wireless infrastructure so we can be up and running immediately, rather than waiting for the last mile of the communications connection.

Effective collaboration also requires better understanding of terminology. At one level, as an industry we will have to set standards to define what terms such as "plug-and-play" really mean. More fundamentally, the industry is blighted by misinterpretation and poor translation. When tenants speak to owners about taking retail space, they do so from a business perspective—they perceive the space in the context of how it will help them sell goods and create a customer experience. The owners, however, tend to think simply in terms of square footage. In order to collaborate effectively, the two sides need to be speaking the same business language.

It is easy to talk about cross-industry collaboration in principle, of course, but far harder to make it happen. There are, however, a number of initiatives that will ease the transition. First, there is an urgent need for a cross-industry consortium. There are plenty of consortia in architecture and design, and a number of industry bodies elsewhere, but we need a group that spans the different participants and pulls their different interests together.

Second, we should look to extend the use of building-information management and visualisation, so that they cover the entire lifecycle. At HOCHTIEF, we have developed a virtual-construction software application that allows us to model buildings prior to construction, and these technologies help us understand, from the very beginning, what we are setting out to accomplish from a business

Virtual Design and Construction model

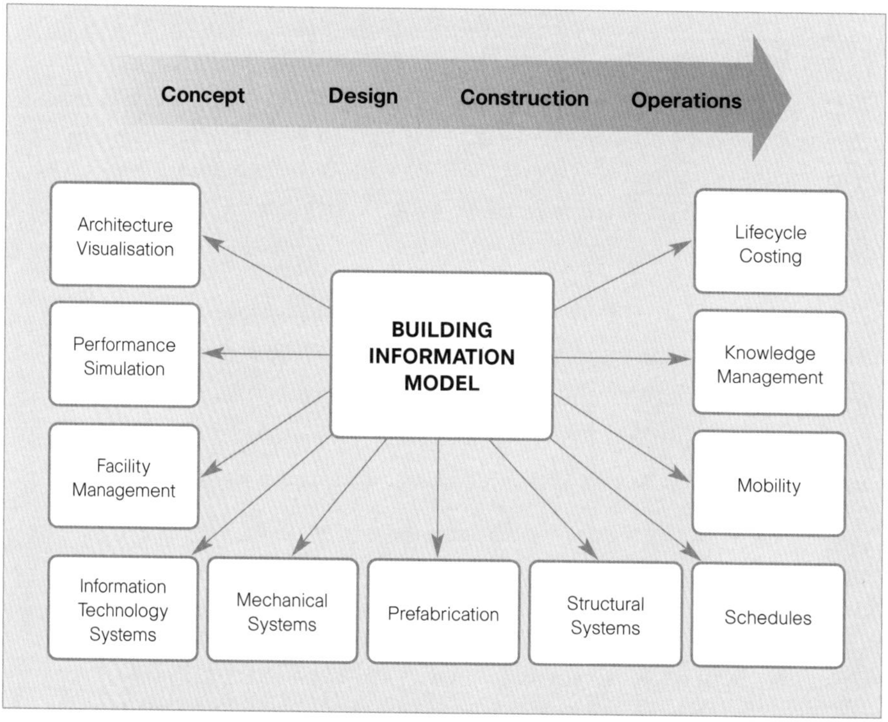

Figure 1 Virtual Design and Construction (ViCon) describes the procedure of planning and simulating the construction and operation of a building with the help of 3-D computer models. These models cover the entire lifecycle of a building, thus providing for both time and cost savings. Source: Cisco, 2006.

perspective during the entire building lifecycle. We need to anticipate the way occupants will repurpose the space, both with and without plug-and-play capability. Using this digital model, we can build properties, address potential limitations in usage, and significantly reduce construction and operation costs further down the line.

Virtual Design and Construction allows us to model prior to construction what we want to accomplish from a business perspective during the entire building lifecycle.

We are also focusing hard on capturing information from the modelling and construction projects so that we can share information—another example of repeatable uniqueness. If we are building a hospital, for example, we would benefit significantly if we had a database holding details of similar projects that we have carried out in the past, giving us pointers for the best approach based on climate, the mix of hospital activities, and so forth. But the information sharing goes much further. Information is being lost across the entire building lifecycle, from concept, through design and build, to operation. Each stage generates information that is vital to retain. During the concept stage, assumptions are generated about the project, which translate into design criteria, and are then turned into product. When you arrive at the facilities-management stage, all of that information is relevant because it informs activities, such as preventative or corrective maintenance.

This collaborative environment will trigger significant change among construction companies, which will tend to diverge into two groups. Some will continue to play a role as specialists. Others, including HOCHTIEF and Turner, will expand their presence across the building lifecycle, playing a more collaborative role from concept to facilities management, and providing advisory services to owners using digital tools such as building-information models.

DR. BERNHARD BÜRKLIN

HEAD OF CORPORATE DEVELOPMENT, HOCHTIEF, GERMANY

Dr. Bernard Bürklin started his career at HOCHTIEF in 1980 as a design engineer in the Technical Department of Civil Engineering, and from 1981 to 1987 he worked on numerous construction sites abroad. From 1990 to 1992 he worked as a project manager for HOCHTIEF and was responsible for the extension of Warsaw International Airport. Dr. Bürklin subsequently developed the Controlling Center and the Corporate Development Center at HOCHTIEF corporate headquarters.

From 1999 to 2001, Dr. Bürklin was a member of the management board of HOCHTIEF International; in this function, he worked as executive vice president of The Turner Corporation in New York. From 2001 to 2004, he was a member of the executive board of HOCHTIEF Construction AG, with responsibility for the Market Segment Groups as well as for risk management and information technology. In 2003, he managed the RWE exit special project on behalf of the executive board of HOCHTIEF Holding. Since 2004, Dr. Bürklin has been head of the company's Strategic Corporation Development Department.

Dr. Bürklin studied civil engineering at Munich Technical University and obtained his doctorate at the university's Faculty for Tunneling and Construction Operations.

1

2

3

4

5

6

Photography / Digital Images

1 & 2 **Department Store, Cologne**
A transparent glass facade is a perfect presentation medium for Peek & Cloppenburg, surrounding the ever-changing fashion with ease. Advanced technology, environmentally friendly materials, and digital building controls are widely deployed.

Architect: Renzo Piano, owner and operator, Brilar Beteiligungs GmbH + Co. Vermietungs KG München; General Contractor: HOCHTIEF Construction AG Düsseldorf; Supporting Framework and Heating and Cooling Technology by HOCHTIEF, 2005. Photo © Andreas Fechner, Peek & Cloppenburg KG Düsseldorf

3 & 4 **4-D Modeling**
The basis for all applications under Virtual Design and Construction (ViCon) is a three-dimensional computer model which, when enhanced by additional information, is used as a four-dimensional (4-D) model for a variety of tasks. Graphic 4-D models significantly simplify communication and coordination between the project stakeholders. These models cover the entire lifecycle of a building, thus providing for both time and cost savings.

Source: HOCHTIEF, 2006

5 **Clash Detection**
Before physical construction of a building begins, a digital model is built to detect possible construction conflicts. The building information model facilitates optimum coordination of the individual building systems, such as the mechanical and structural systems shown here.

Source: HOCHTIEF, 2006

6 **Interactive Workroom**
Interactive Workspaces called i-rooms are new ways for people to work together for task-oriented projects, such as brainstorming, and design and construction progress reviews. This i-room is located offsite and is equipped with computing and interaction devices, from large digital displays to handheld PCs and wireless devices.

Source: HOCHTIEF, 2006

ADVANCED TECHNOLOGY assists us with integrating social, economic, and environmental sustainability requirements into our building and urban designs.

James R. Brogan

SENIOR ASSOCIATE PRINCIPAL AND DIRECTOR, FIRMWIDE INFORMATION AND TECHNOLOGY, KOHN PEDERSEN FOX ASSOCIATES, UNITED STATES

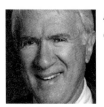

A. Eugene Kohn

CHAIRMAN, KOHN PEDERSEN FOX ASSOCIATES, UNITED STATES

Connectivity in building design

CITIES ARE LIVING COMMUNITIES that continually change, and the architects who alter the urban landscape have far-reaching responsibilities. The buildings we architects create should both draw from their surroundings—out of respect for local traditions—and be a catalyst for change, embracing innovations that improve people's livelihood and social surroundings. Whether we are focusing on an individual workplace or the environmental concerns of an entire community, our designs must address a cross section of needs.

FOR THE PAST 30 YEARS, we at Kohn Pedersen Fox Architects (KPF) have designed buildings and spaces that provide an uplifting backdrop for daily life. We have a global presence, with offices in New York, London, and Shanghai, and over 400 employees. Our designs use new construction techniques, innovative building components, and advanced technologies to make buildings more useful and efficient. The techniques are validated through our own research and development efforts. We consider social, economic, and environmental sustainability requirements within our creative efforts, and employ advanced technology tools to assist us with integrating these considerations into our building and urban design processes. The results of our design work must increase value for building owners and users.

Our strategic investments in innovation make us unusual in a conservative building industry. These investments give us new ideas, products, and work methods, which increase our productivity, boost value for our clients, and improve the quality of life for the public. Technology facilitates connectivity and collaboration, and is a fundamental component of our practice. Connectivity takes three forms in our practice: connectivity of our global design practice; connectivity among the collaborative project team of clients, consultants, fabricators, contractors, subcontractors, and operators; and connectivity within the building as the "fourth utility" to integrate and unify services and support.

Digital design tools

Technology innovation has led to advanced information management and three-dimensional modeling techniques that help us improve our understanding of the architectural, cost, constructional, and operational implications of our designs. This understanding benefits our clients directly by streamlining processes for better alignment with client project schedules; by improving coordination and document accuracy throughout the project team; by tapping into best practices that improve efficiency and productivity; and by generating higher-value designs, using tools to investigate and evaluate design options.

Our technology group, which spans our firm, develops digital design tools that extend the capabilities of established three-dimensional design techniques. These tools enable us to explore more design options and iterations in shorter amounts of time. We use the computer not only for visualization, analysis, and evaluation, but also for the generation of designs within predefined parameters, which could be geometric, environmental, materials-driven, site-related, or program-driven. In this way, our design computation specialist group can explore a wider range of design permutations within a fixed range of boundaries, while informing designers of ramifications of each option with real-time feedback. We can also pull in a wide range of data, including performance data and environmental factors, to help inform designs.

Technology innovation has led to advanced information management and three-dimensional modeling techniques that help us improve our understanding of the architectural, cost, constructional, and operational implications of our designs.

We are extending these processes and tools beyond the specialist group to our project teams, gradually infusing these elements into our standard design methodologies. One example is the retail development in Tianjin, China. While designing an elliptical retail space, we used

Figure 1 A series of building design alternatives, as shown in this picture, can be rapidly fabricated using tools that "print" physical study models from the digital building model as easily as printing a copy of a drawing on paper. Architect: Kohn Pedersen Fox, 2004.

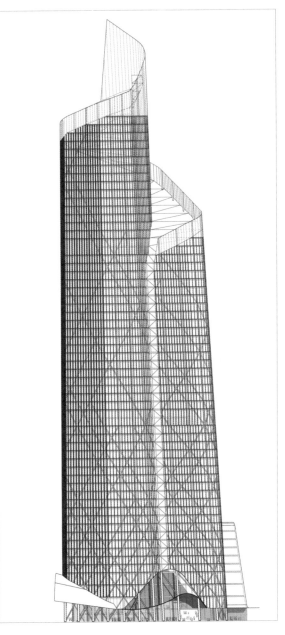

Figure 2 For study and design purposes, Kohn Pedersen Fox (KPF) created digital models of Bishopsgate Tower, which will be London's tallest building at 1,008 feet high. Linked to a parametric model containing robust design data instead of just geometric information, the 3-D model aids real-time design. On this project and others, KPF has made extensive use of visualization and modeling software along with geospatial data. The project was commissioned by the German developer and fund manager DIFA. Source: Kohn Pedersen Fox, 2004.

parametric tools to adjust the design to minimize variances in glass shape and size. Tweaking the design allowed us to standardize the size of many of the glass panels, reduce the number of custom shapes and sizes, and control costs.

In tandem with our parametric modeling processes, we also employ rapid prototyping tools in our design-evaluation process. These tools allow us to move from three-dimensional digital designs to physical designs with resin or powder-based materials. The tools "print" physical study models from the computer-generated design models as easily as printing them on paper. We used these tools while designing the China State Construction International Tower in Shanghai, China. This building has a reverse taper—it gets wider as it rises—making it a complex geometric challenge. The glass panels in the external curtain wall are, potentially, of varying sizes, which could possibly be an expensive fabrication and construction concern. We initially modeled the tower using typical three-dimensional tools, then scripted our parametric tools to examine the impact of different design options, discovering in a few moments how a small design change might affect the size, shape, and volume of the glass panels. Due to the tools we were using, we could identify and describe each piece of glass in three-dimensional space, and then deliver the information directly to the contractor. The final construction documents contained both written specifications and the three-dimensional building model.

Environmental-sustainability simulation

Our practice is creating new methods to help our clients reduce both energy costs and building-lifecycle costs. Our core design processes have integrated concepts that support environmental sustainability. Digital connectivity allows us to study the environmental performance from early design stages. For example, environmental simulation and computational fluid-dynamics software study a project's response to wind and air flow to inform and define environmental parameters. We are integrating these tools into our desktop PC software to benefit our designs. Our three-dimensional models also generate information about solar energy, heating, and ways to optimize building facades and forms to enhance their environmental efficiency.

The new headquarters for the Spanish energy provider Endesa in Madrid is one example of this approach. The brief for the design made it clear that the company wanted to improve its brand with respect to the environment. One of the key design objectives was, therefore, to support Endesa's ambition by providing a sustainable approach to environmental design issues.

Our practice is creating new methods to help our clients reduce both energy costs and building-lifecycle costs.

Knowledge management

We are harnessing the vast project knowledge gained from our extensive global project experiences by creating a database that our employees can use locally, in projects anywhere in the world.

The KPF intranet contains a portal for many of our applications and day-to-day tools, including templates, design standards, and modeling processes. It also provides a forum for stimulating internal dialogue among our offices to discuss particular building types and determine best practices for addressing similar issues. It includes a massive amount of reference materials such as an image repository and project database, information about new building materials, and details about company resources. Specific project information on the intranet is particularly valuable.

The portal's project-update section gives any member of our staff—in any of our offices—access to information about current projects. A central database houses unique information about our building projects and includes project descriptions, images, materials, plans, and models. It provides insights into design performance and guidelines for future projects. This capability is helpful because it allows us to take advantage of this knowledge for new projects with similar scope or with repeat clientele.

The portal is a resource that evolves continuously, and we are expanding the amount of skills-based information available online. Today, we can search the project database to find out who has worked on specific projects and to locate people with specialist expertise. We are planning future tools that will allow us to drill down to very specific expertise and focused skill sets.

Our vision is to extend this repository into project-specific portals, allowing KPF staff, associated external project teams, and our clients to log in from anywhere for real-time designs and specifications. We also plan to integrate these portals tightly with business intelligence tools.

Collaborative building process

Our own designers and project teams have first-hand experience with the technical capabilities that we are embedding into our buildings— wireless data access, wide area network connectivity of our three offices, PDA integration, videoconferencing, Web conferencing, and collaboration technologies delivered to the desktop—because we deploy these technologies within our own practice.

Connectivity is not limited to our practice. It extends outward as well, facilitating real-time communication among building teams and supporting collaboration among the client, architect, various consultants, and contractors on a project. Sharing the three-dimensional model for specific analysis with team consultants—such as the structural engineer, the mechanical engineer, the acoustic engineer, the lighting consultant, the contractor, as well as the estimator, contractor, and fabricator—fosters greater collaboration and design synchronization, translating into more efficient construction and adherence to the overall project schedule.

Integrated practice

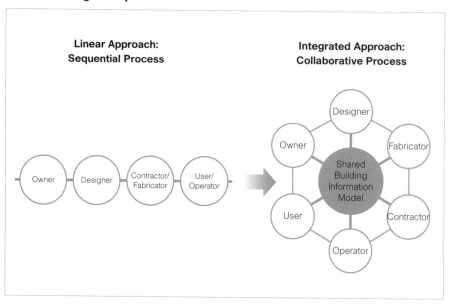

Figure 3 Sharing the digital Building Information Model (BIM) with the entire design team fosters greater collaboration and design integration, translating into a more efficient design and construction process. Source: Cisco, 2006.

Network resources also extend to KPF construction sites, using a laptop, tablet PC, or PDA with wireless broadband services. Now, we can immediately address changes, conflicts, and questions with the architectural office to mitigate construction delays and their associated expense. The construction trailer is no longer a disconnected entity, but an extension of the design team.

Building-program transformation

End-user mobility and collaboration are transforming building programs and our architecture. Local and remote communications allow us to design and construct buildings that provide access to a central network of resources independent of location. The pervasiveness of data access has a significant impact on our designs, regardless of building type. Changing work patterns, more flexible social interactions, and work being accomplished in a variety of locations all affect building functions, users, and user services. We can interact more easily with one another because we are not restricted to performing tasks in a specific place. With mobility, however, comes the need to create space for casual, impromptu meetings alongside traditional meeting rooms for formal gatherings. Architects can no longer think in terms of fixed spaces with fixed purposes; what might be a meeting room in the morning could be used for working solo, for conference calls, or for training sessions in the afternoon, and for videoconferencing in the evening. Our designs must enable this flexibility.

Changing work patterns, flexible social interactions, and work being accomplished in a variety of locations all affect building functions, services, and designs.

We recently designed a new building at the Wharton School of the University of Pennsylvania. Among the architectural requirements, the brief outlined a visionary strategy for integration of wired and wireless data access for faculty and students in both classrooms and social spaces. Every piece of IT hardware—from large plasma screens to student laptops—is connected, both inside the building and in the open spaces surrounding it, making everyone part of the same social hub.

Building-fabric evolution

Finally, connectivity technologies are becoming embedded in the fabric of our buildings. The value of connectivity to the client and building owner continues into postoccupancy by exploiting the communications data network as the fourth utility to add real-time management of the entire building lifecycle. This unified digital platform enables the building to become a source of information itself, as we explored with the Morgan Stanley Building in New York City, where light-emitting diodes in the facade communicate changing media content. The fourth utility extends to campuses and the urban infrastructure network, such as in our New Songdo City project in South Korea for our client, Gale International. (See essay, "New Songdo City: Building Experiences, Interactions, and a New Way of Living," page 182.)

There are many advantages of a unified interbuilding data network:

- The convergence of IT infrastructure and property infrastructure enables virtualized services such as tenant portals, concierge, and maintenance and support services

- Technology tools monitor the building system performance, automatically adjusting them as needed

- Technology tools monitor and regulate energy and resource usage

- Habit monitoring and behavior recognition are enabled by using wireless microsensor networks to "learn" when and how occupants use spaces and to align services with usage

- Sensors for light, heat, and building IT services are adjusted automatically or by users in each space

- Technology monitors equipment health and services, signaling early warnings of equipment failure

- Support, repairs, and maintenance are faster with more integrated crew support through wireless technology

- Radio frequency identification (RFID) tags monitor equipment, visitors, and building occupants for security and safety

- Integrated, data-rich, intelligent three-dimensional building models manage, monitor, and support buildings and their users

By integrating their own management tools into the digital building information model, clients, and owners can exploit our rich knowledge base to operate and manage their buildings more effectively. Collaborative and connected technologies make a continuum of capabilities available to everyone involved in the building lifecycle:

- Using computer-generated design databases to inform and guide designers through the creative process of building design

- Enabling collaboration with the project team using this information-rich model, specific to their disciplines

- Allowing contractors to use the model database for estimating material quantity and budget, scheduling, building simulation, and full-scale fabrication

- Facilitating and streamlining building operations, maintenance, and lifecycle management

Realizing the vision

At the core of the technology evolution is the need for the seamless exchange and management of digital information among all stakeholders in the building value chain. The lack of interoperability among computer-aided design, engineering, and management software systems is estimated to cost the building industry US$60 billion each year globally.[1] Owners and operators bear about two-thirds of this expense directly. Sharing the digital building information model with contractors who add their data, use it to directly drive manufacturing and fabrication, and provide this data to the client as a tool for building management is a sophisticated process already emerging today.

Realizing this vision requires collaboration, connectivity, and interoperability. We predict that over the next decade, we will see greater integration of the design, construction, and operation teams that rely on these digital building models and information-rich knowledge databases, which can be used in building management. And behind it all is connectivity, which is redefining design and construction processes and extending them to benefit our built environment, defining state-of-the-art building practices worldwide.

---

1. *Key Trends in the Construction Industry* (McGraw-Hill Construction, 2006). Based on Michael P. Gallaher, Alan C. O'Connor, John L. Dettbarn, Jr., and Linda T. Gilday, *Cost Analysis of Inadequate Interoperability in the U.S. Capital Facilities Industry* (National Institute of Standards and Technology, 2004).

JAMES R. BROGAN

SENIOR ASSOCIATE PRINCIPAL AND DIRECTOR, FIRMWIDE INFORMATION TECHNOLOGY, KOHN PEDERSEN FOX ASSOCIATES, UNITED STATES

James R. Brogan is the director of Information Technology at Kohn Pedersen Fox Associates (KPF), overseeing all aspects of technology for KPF's three locations: New York, London, and Shanghai. Areas of technology Brogan manages include the KPF internal and wide-area network infrastructure, firmwide knowledge databases, Web/Internet technologies, production standards, the firmwide intranet, and design software strategies including parametric and performance-based 3-D modeling tools and Building Information Model/computer-aided design technologies. Brogan also works directly with the project teams as technology liaison to determine technology requirements, develop project-specific guidelines, and help ensure integration of technology with the project.

Brogan is a registered architect in the State of New York and a member of the American Institute of Architects (AIA). He is the former 2001 chair and 2000 vice chair of the National AIA Technology in Architectural Practice Committee, a member of the AIA CIO Large Firm Roundtable, and is the former chair and vice chair of the New York AIA Information Technology Committee from 1995 to 1999.

Brogan has a bachelor of architecture degree from Pratt Institute, in New York, and taught at New York's Parsons School of Design in the Masters of Architecture program from 1991 to 1999.

A. EUGENE KOHN

CHAIRMAN, KOHN PEDERSEN FOX ASSOCIATES, UNITED STATES

A. Eugene Kohn currently serves as chairman of Kohn Pedersen Fox (KPF) Associates. In 1976, along with William Pedersen and Sheldon Fox, Kohn founded KPF based on a commitment to design excellence. Since then, Kohn has served as partner and is in charge of a number of KPF's major domestic and international projects. He is also responsible for many of the firm's new commissions. Since its inception, KPF has earned six national American Institute of Architects (AIA) design awards and, in 1990, became the youngest firm ever to be presented with the AIA Architectural Firm Award.

Kohn has been honored by the National Education Fund (1997) and the Sheltering Arms Children Service (1995). He has also been presented with the Sidney L. Strauss Award from the New York Society of Architects (1996), and the Lifetime Achievement Award given by the Wharton Real Estate Center (1997). In 1998, he was recognized with the Ellis Island Medal of Honor, and in 2002 was presented with the Harry B. Rutkins Award from the AIA New York Chapter. Recently, Kohn received the 2003 Business Leadership Award from the Burden Center for the Aging, Inc., for his accomplishments in both business and the community. In 2005, Kohn received the Salvadori Award for Excellence in Design, and in 2006 was inducted into the Central High School hall of fame in Philadelphia.

Kohn has degrees from the University of Pennsylvania. He attended the Harvard Graduate School of Design's Real Estate Development Course in 1982, and is an executive fellow of the Advanced Management Development Program in Real Estate at Harvard's Graduate School of Design—the first architect to be awarded the title.

In addition, Kohn is a fellow of the American Institute of Architects and a member of its Octagon Society. During 1988, he served as president of the AIA New York City Chapter. He is also a member of the Royal Institute of British Architects, the Council on Tall Buildings and Urban Habitat, the Japan Institute of Architects, as well as an honorary member of the Fellows of the Philippine Institute.

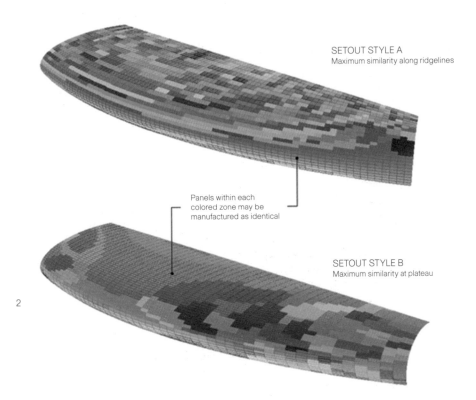

1

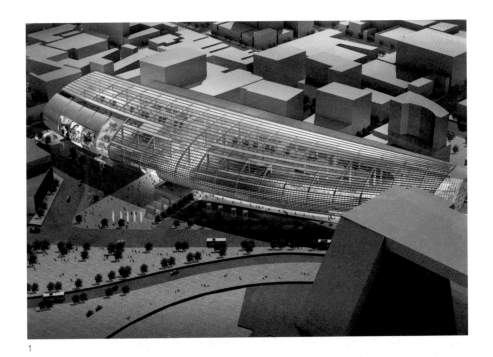

SETOUT STYLE A
Maximum similarity along ridgelines

Panels within each
colored zone may be
manufactured as identical

SETOUT STYLE B
Maximum similarity at plateau

2

3

4

Photography / Digital Images

1 Tianjin Hang Lung Plaza, Tianjin, China
Digital visualizations, as the one shown for this retail development in
Tianjin, China, are used early in the design process to communicate
effectively with clients and the building design stakeholders.

Architect: Kohn Pedersen Fox, 2004

2 Panel Analysis
The building facade analysis of a retail development in Tianjin, China,
uses digital design tools to minimize the variances in glass panel
shape and size, as represented by the different color coding. This
approach enables better cost control of the fabrication of building
components and the construction of complex building shapes.

Architect: Kohn Pedersen Fox, 2004

3 Morgan Stanley Dean Witter Building, New York, United States
The changeable nature of light-emitting diode technology, combined
with connectivity and media content, turns building facades into
media for architectural communication, as illustrated by the Morgan
Stanley Dean Witter Building in New York.

Architect: Kohn Pedersen Fox, 2004

4 Endesa Headquarters, Madrid, Spain
The new headquarters for the Spanish utility company Endesa
combines innovative design and cutting-edge technology to create
an exciting new workplace for the Endesa employees, to set a new
standard in environmentally responsible architecture, and to improve
the Endesa brand with respect to corporate social responsibility.

Architect: Kohn Pedersen Fox, 2004

PERFORMANCE-BASED DESIGN

is a collaborative design approach that is joined with sophisticated computer analysis and 3-D simulations.

Terry Hill
CHAIRMAN, ARUP GROUP, UNITED KINGDOM

Chris Luebkeman
DIRECTOR FOR GLOBAL FORESIGHT AND INNOVATION, ARUP GROUP
UNITED KINGDOM

Performance-Based Design and connected practice

ARUP IS A GLOBAL FIRM OF DESIGNERS, engineers, planners and business consultants providing a diverse range of professional services to clients around the world. It is a wholly independent organisation, owned in trust on behalf of its staff. With no external shareholders, it has an independence that enables it to shape its own direction with no outside pressure or influence. The course it has chosen focuses on Performance-Based Design as a key mode of operation, underpinned by a completely connected practice. We are the creative force behind some of the most innovative and sustainable designs globally, and our worldwide corporate and public clients are as wide-ranging as our projects. Arup is probably best known for some of the world's most outstanding buildings, including the Opera House in Sydney, the Pompidou Centre in Paris and the Water Cube for the Beijing Olympics (see photograph 1: Water Cube). Through an innovative and fully integrated approach, which brings our full complement of skills and knowledge to bear on design problems, we exert significant influence on the built environment.

PERFORMANCE-BASED DESIGN (PBD) is a core result of our design philosophy, which aims to develop solutions that integrate disciplines and skills to deliver holistic solutions. Put simply, it means that we look for solutions to enable optimum performance of projects from the point of view of both clients and users—including clients' operational requirements and resulting financial risks—rather than simply following a specification. It is important for us to establish a collaborative relationship with our clients that enables us to produce the best buildings for their business needs. PBD helps us accomplish this through a collaborative, multidisciplinary design approach that is joined with sophisticated computer analysis and three-dimensional (3-D) simulations.

45

A collaborative design approach

The economic and social losses caused by recent major earthquakes have forced the international earthquake engineering community to re-examine the objectives for earthquake-resistant design. Many codes aim to protect occupants against building collapses but do not attempt to deliver any specific structural or nonstructural performance outside of that. This makes it difficult to assess operational or financial risk.

The concept of PBD responds directly to this issue: it provides clients with a one-stop service to produce a truly reliable earthquake-tolerant structure, and it assesses the likelihood of performance more accurately than standard methods. It also allows clients to agree with the design team on a set of performance criteria for their structures (for example, "The structure will remain operational after a moderate earthquake and not collapse under a maximum credible earthquake.") Such a procedure can minimise lifecycle costs and produce client-sensitive structures.

The life-blood of Performance-Based Design is the collection and storage of large quantities of information.

By setting performance-based requirements, our clients are agreeing on parameters rather than dictating absolutes. This gives our design team the scope to readdress the problem, conceive a fresh solution and, therefore, challenge previous thinking. Our approach to building design in seismic zones, for example, has benefited from our experience in Japan, where we applied 3-D, nonlinear time-history analysis to several building projects between 1988 and 1996. We were successful in gaining the approval of the Ministry of Construction Review. This enabled us to perform the seismic design of the Center for Clinical Sciences Research building at Stanford University using a performance-based methodology—a first in California when the laboratory was completed in 2000.

Another example was the design and construction of a factory that packages fruit juice sold through supermarkets. Six months into the job, the client told us the project had been canceled. When we asked why, we discovered that our client's competitor had undercut them and they had lost the supermarket contract as a result. On further questioning, we learned the contract was canceled because the client could not supply the product cheaply enough. The difference between our client and the competitor was two pence (approximately four cents) per box of juice. As a result, we reduced the size of the building and, with a lower capital outlay, our client was able to reduce the price of juice and keep the supermarket contract. This is a prime example of the strength of the Performance-Based Design approach. Because we understood the ultimate goal required by the client, we could offer solutions based on need rather than on a dry building specification. And, we learned a lot about designing the process to be more efficient while delivering improved quality.

There are several enabling prerequisites for our PBD philosophy, key among which is a process of intensive client collaboration. Developing, designing, constructing and operating a building is a complex and specialised process, and many clients do not have a clear idea of what they want. Some might be managers of museums or galleries or impresarios who cannot reasonably be expected to have building-specification expertise. Others overspecify, which is natural for those clients who are either part of or close to the building industry. For example, a railway operator is likely to detail the amounts and types of materials, such as steel and concrete, being delivered. What we would prefer to deal with is a working specification that includes what kind of traffic the railway will carry, how fast it will travel and what level of safety is expected.

Computer analysis and 3-D simulations

Those of us in the real estate and construction industry probably find it easier through experience to visualise a building from drawings, but for others it can be very hard. We now use 3-D design tools extensively throughout the design process, along with interactive virtual environments. This helps us simulate building environments, move away from purely rectilinear shapes, and design and prefabricate components that fit together precisely in the field (see photograph 5: CCTV Beijing).

The life-blood of PBD is the collection and storage of large quantities of information. Among the benefits is the ability to create 3-D simulations, which give clients a representation of what the ultimate solutions or potential options may be. This then allows us, together with the client, to interact with that potential solution in a very visual way and to proceed toward a mutually agreeable decision (see image 3: Amsterdam Public Library).

The planning process for federal courthouses in the United States is one example of how we use 3-D simulations in our design process. There used to be a requirement that a plywood mock-up had to be constructed before any new courthouse was built. This allowed the judge to feel his or her courtroom seat, assess sightlines and so on. Yet in 2005, we managed to convince the federal administration to accept our 3-D visualisation instead, saving time and money

Consider the auto industry as another example. To sell cars around the world, automakers must crash test them in almost every potential market. This adds up to a lot of cars in the garbage heap. Instead of destroying resources, we can simulate the crash tests in 3-D. This way, car manufacturers can streamline their processes; they have to crash only six cars, for instance, instead of approximately 100.

In addition, our simulations are highly technical—a computer simulation that models every weld and bolt can take up to 50 hours on a supercomputer. We validated our approach by comparing a real crash test with our simulations. We found that the wrinkles in the metal and the damage to the paintwork were effectively identical. Apart from the cost savings and time savings, digital models allow subsequent analysis that would not have been possible with a live test. For instance, we can make components invisible in the simulation so testers can see what happens to the engine mountings and the crumple zones. In one analysis we cut out the fuel tank so that we could see the fuel sloshing around without the tank hampering the view (see image 4: Crash-Test Analysis Model).

In today's global, round-the-clock business environment, connectivity is core to the process of sharing and building knowledge.

While these simulations are innovative and productive, it is our SoundLab that is one of the most exciting developments in the area of simulated 3-D environments. We believe that we are at the forefront of acoustics in this area. We have four sound rooms around the globe—New York, London, Melbourne and Hong Kong—that can simulate, among other things, the acoustical environment of major concert halls around the world—from the Sydney Opera House to the Royal Albert Hall in London. The SoundLabs provide an interactive experience that makes occupants feel as though they are listening to music in a real concert hall. A client may have a concept of the sound quality required for a particular performance space, and our SoundLab allows the client to work with the design team to "tune" their space as they wish before one brick is laid. The global aspect of this client collaboration is critical; we can place the client in one room and our team in another and, no matter where each party is, they can discuss the project while reconfiguring the acoustics as if they had a face-to-face experience (see photograph 2: New York SoundLab).

The connected practice

In today's global, round-the-clock business environment, connectivity is core to the process of sharing and building knowledge both internally and with clients. We think of connectivity in four dimensions: people, process, technology and projects. Our work is project-based. To deliver these projects, we focus on enhancing value in three areas: people, process and technology.

People

People are our greatest resource. It sounds like a cliché, perhaps, but for us it is true: they represent our offer, our differentiator and our strength. We are very keen on people sharing all information that might be relevant to the project. Our global network means that to get an answer, all anyone needs to do is pick up the phone and dial five digits or send an e-mail. Within Arup, information is free at the point of use. We encourage individuals to share both professional and personal information. This kind of information-led approach, underpinned by connectivity, has numerous benefits. One real-world example of the benefits of this approach was seen when we built a bonsai museum for one of our clients. Our comprehensive database told us we had a bonsai expert in the firm; he joined the project team and helped us get close to the client and make a better product.

This emphasis on information sharing not only resolves professional issues—but also creates bonds between coworkers. If an engineer who happens to be a keen sailor moves to a new office halfway across the globe, our intranet allows him to search the local corporate community for others with similar interests. Just as important, when measuring individuals' performance, the one element we consciously do not measure is specific skills because we believe this encourages hoarding, not sharing. While there remains some reluctance on the part of some technicians and technologists to share their expertise, I am convinced we can change this over time. One of our biggest cultural challenges is making people aware that they can ask for help without it being considered a sign of weakness.

We can learn two key lessons from the cultural change: the first is making people feel good about working for Arup; the second is helping them collaborate effectively for the purpose of getting the job done. We encourage easy ways of networking and easy ways of reaching out and speaking to people. Individuals are allowed to manage their own environment so that they're in control. This is important at a corporate level and also at an individual level. These elements help build a team that is global in its reach and works like an organisation in the real world with clients.

Process

Today, we can share processes around the world. For instance, knowledge developed by one office in response to local client needs can be transferred easily to other locations. This high degree of connectivity also helps us to centralise and standardise some working practices and client offerings across geographies.

We use our technology infrastructure to discuss most of our biggest projects in real-time interactions. One example is the 2008 Summer Olympics in Beijing, where we are involved with building swimming pools, stadia, airports, convention centres and the like. These large-scale projects are managed from a variety of different offices depending on where our expertise resides. For instance, I can review on my London computer screen the work of a designer in Beijing in real time. These projects are what we call global/local—projects using a combination of global tools and technology such as the intranet, videoconferencing and application sharing—to deliver a local product to a local client through geographically distributed teams.

We use our technology infrastructure to discuss most of our biggest projects in real-time interactions.

Connectivity now underpins all of our projects. One of the best examples occurred when we won the Brisbane Airport contract. We had just completed the tender documents to build a new runway at London's Stansted Airport, a huge job for which to prepare. Within days of Arup winning this contract, we received a request for a proposal to expand the Brisbane Airport. We were able to use our Stansted Airport experience to prove only 10 days later that Arup was the company that should be awarded the Brisbane contract. We won for three reasons: one, the levels of information we possessed about the topic; two, the skill sets of our people and the technology infrastructure that enabled them to deliver; three, the connectivity that allowed us to provide a knowledge transfer from one big project to another. In particular, the technology enabled us to react quickly. In the old days, it took quite some time to get client information delivered to produce attractive brochures and to distribute the documentation to Arup's offices around the world. It could take up to a year for the experience of one job to percolate throughout the organisation and then allow us to manage another similar one. Connectivity enabled us to compress that knowledge-sharing time and to interact effectively.

Terminal 4 at New York's John F. Kennedy International Airport is an example where we exploited both our connectivity and the benefits of being a global organisation that can allocate work internally to countries with the right skill sets to gain an economic advantage. Much of the airport was designed in our office in Zimbabwe. Because of (or maybe in spite of) the political situation there, our employees are highly skilled and motivated people. So we shipped a lot of work there rather than outsourcing it. At the same time, we kept the local practice going because there was no other local work at that time. In general, this is an example of how we use our low-cost centres within Arup and how we outsource very little of our core product—only payroll and similar administrative processes.

Technology

We first used computers in the late 1950s, particularly in our work on the designs of the iconic Sydney Opera House. Not only were we the first U.K. engineering consultants to install an in-house computer, but we were also one of the first in the world to install an IBM mainframe in the early 1970s. It was housed in the main building's basement where white-coat acolytes tended the machines in an air-conditioned room.

We now have a modern information and communications infrastructure that is open to all 7,000 employees—engineers, economists and ecologists, amongst others. We are fully connected, and we provide mobility solutions where appropriate. Our intranet grew organically: informal networks and communities of interest started to exploit the new technology when it was first available in the 1990s. It evolved over the past years into an organised business tool, harnessing the best of the tools that have been trial tested by the firm's self-elected beta testers. This evolution took place despite early scepticism by more conservative members of our organisation who found it hard to see the usefulness of technology such as e-mail. Yet, we can no longer imagine our work life without the ubiquitous access and availability of information and communications technologies.

Technology, however, is only the enabler. At our core is the importance that Arup places on its people.

The applications and tools that enable our day-to-day business processes are varied. Videoconferencing constitutes an important component. We have videoconferencing suites around the world, and the number of individual units on people's desks is growing. For instance, I use our videoconferencing tool to interact with our board members around the world every month for about an hour from my workstation in London. Today's experience is very close to a face-to-face meeting. The full suite of networked tools gives us rapid yet reasoned response. For example, we had a problem with one project where a building was leaning because of certain types of ground conditions. Within half an hour we had resolved the issue because of fast connectivity and the use of our internal bulletin board. With this global search capability we could identify and access appropriate expertise and resources quickly.

Outlook

We see PBD as the clear way forward for developing, planning, constructing, operating and using buildings. This philosophy means that we can deliver more effectively the results that clients need for their business—which is not always what they initially thought was needed.

Technology plays a key role in this process, not just from the point of view of storing information but also from the perspective of distributing, processing and displaying it. As we have seen, 3-D simulations can play a large part in helping clients make business decisions about buildings. This is likely to become a much larger element of the design process. We increasingly use technologies that are delivering ever-greater realism: consumer-level 3-D simulations, interactive games and digital movie animations, amongst others. The ability to view and discuss those simulations and other kinds of information on a global basis is the consequence of Arup's investment in modern connectivity.

Technology, however, is only the enabler. At our core is the importance that Arup places on its people no matter where they are, and in helping them become part of a worldwide team. Without a level of teamwork that gives us a local presence while deploying global experience, Arup would not occupy its preeminent position within the real estate and construction industry.

TERRY HILL

CHAIRMAN, ARUP GROUP, UNITED KINGDOM

Terry Hill is chairman of the Arup Group, a global design and business consultancy. He has responsibility for the overall strategic direction of the firm, and his role is to ensure the delivery of the best in building, infrastructure and technology consulting to clients throughout the world. Hill has made a successful career in Arup, guiding the strategic direction of large, complex and challenging projects.

Hill has a background in civil engineering and economics, and previously led Arup's Infrastructure Division, where his role centred on consulting, infrastructure and managing major schemes.

CHRIS LUEBKEMAN

DIRECTOR OF GLOBAL FORESIGHT AND INNOVATION, ARUP GROUP, UNITED KINGDOM

Chris Luebkeman is a member of Arup's Design and Technical Executive Team, which promotes the highest standards of design and technical skill to ensure that the organization is one of the world's leading practitioners in its chosen fields.

Since joining the firm, Luebkeman has facilitated the creation of an e-commerce strategy, initiated research projects on the "designer's desktop of the future" and encouraged thinking about how to evolve the firm's network from a skills-based network to a knowledge-based network.

Luebkeman has advised the U.K. Government's Environmental and Physical Sciences Research Council on strategic matters relating to the built environment. He sits on the Innovative Manufacturing Centres Evaluation Panel and is guiding the Five-Yearly National Research Review. In 2004, Luebkeman was named a senior fellow at the Design Futures Council.

Educated as a geologist, structural engineer and architect, Luebkeman has a background in research. Before joining Arup, he studied in Switzerland and went on to become a faculty member of the Departments of Architecture at the University of Oregon, the Chinese University of Hong Kong, and Massachusetts Institute of Technology.

1

2

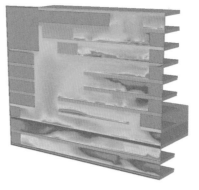

3

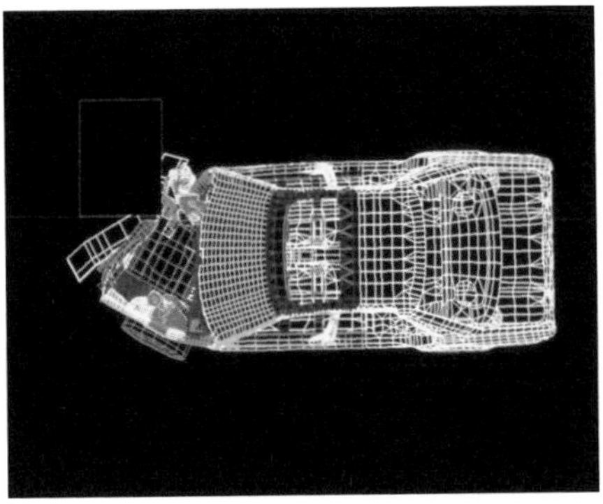

4

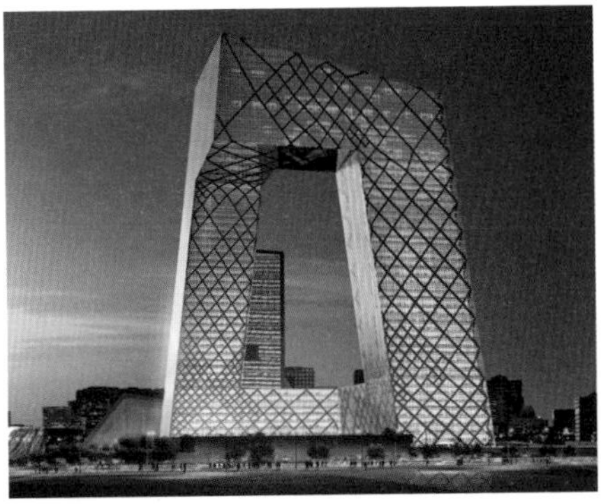

5

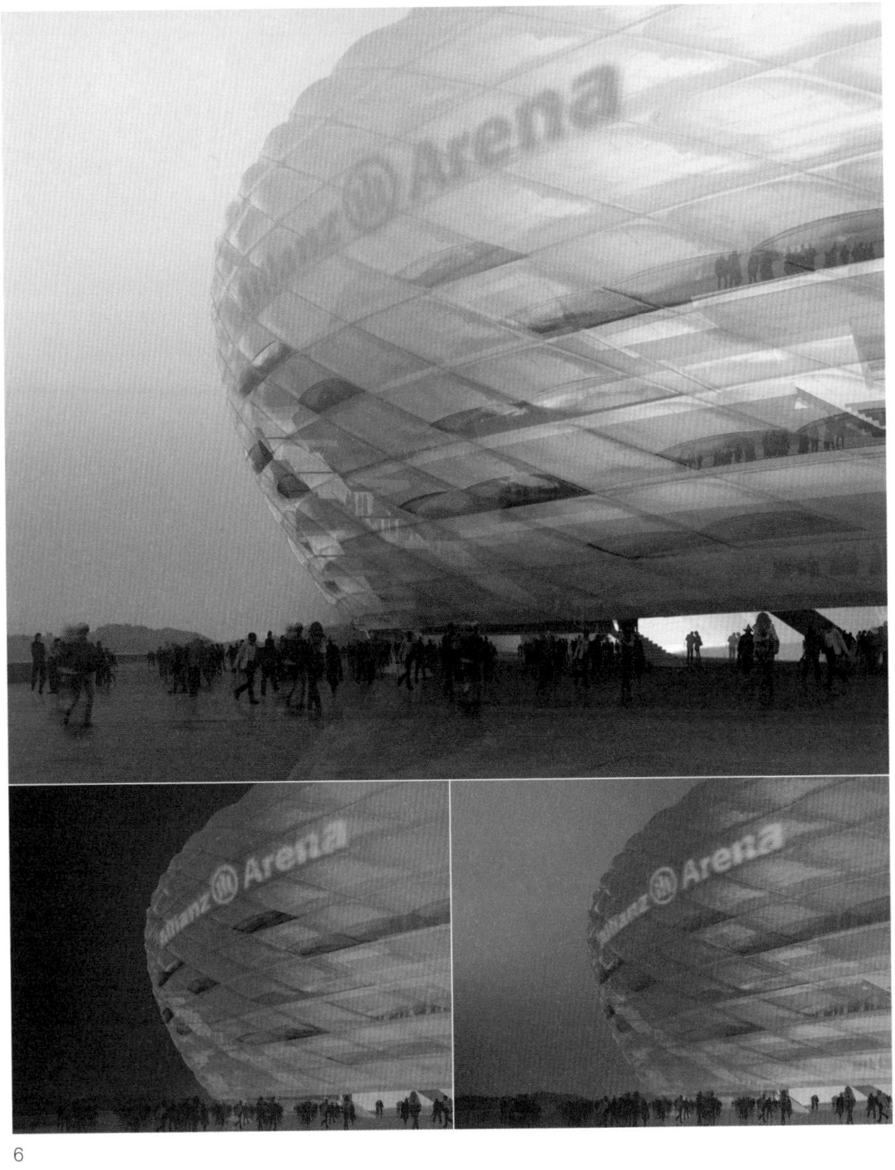

6

1 **Water Cube**
A three-dimensional (3-D) digital model of the Water Cube, a national swimming center under development for the 2008 Summer Olympic Games in Beijing, reveals every object within. The Water Cube, based on a common natural pattern, is the most effective subdivision of three-dimensional space—the fundamental arrangement of organic cells and the natural formation of soap bubbles. Arup extracted all elevations, sections and details to produce the final construction documentation drawings from the 3-D model.

Design team: Arup, PTW Architect, CSCEC (China State Construction and Engineering Corporation), and CSCEC Shenzhen Design Institute, 2003.

Digital Image © Arup

2 **New York SoundLab**
At the Arup SoundLab in New York an interactive experience makes an occupant feel as though he is listening to music in a concert hall. A client may have a concept of the sound quality required for a particular performance space, and the SoundLab allows him to work with the design team to "tune" his space to his requirements before construction begins.

Source: Arup, 2006. Photo © Arup

3 **Amsterdam Public Library**
Computational fluid-dynamics modeling, shown here in a cross section of the Amsterdam Public Library Atrium, is used to analyze fluid air flow. Computer fluid-dynamics modeling contains "comfort" studies of air temperature and velocity in different areas of the building, smoke analysis in the event of a fire, contaminant analysis to review pollution levels, and condensation studies of the windows to test changing climate conditions.

Architect: Jo Coenen & Co., 2003
Digital Image © Arup

4   **Crash-Test Analysis Model**
    Inspired by Arup's work in automobile design, shown here, Arup
    realized that digital analysis models and software that simulates
    vehicle crash tests could also be applied to analyze seismic activity
    in building structures, enabling the design to be improved iteratively
    as though physical prototype tests were being used.

    Source: Arup, 2006
    Digital Image © Arup

5   **China Central Television**
    Arup used a performance-based design approach for China Central
    Television (CCTV) International headquarters. CCTV is one of two
    tall buildings forming the focal point of a major site in the new
    Central Business District in Beijing. Rethinking the 20th-century
    building typology of a high-rise building, CCTV combines space for
    administration, broadcasting studios and program production—
    reinventing the entire business process of TV production.

    Architect: Office for Metropolitan Architecture, 2002
    Digital Image © Arup

6   **Allianz Arena**
    The new home stadium for Munich's two long-standing football
    clubs—the FC Bayern München and TSV 1860 München—is also
    one of the most architecturally unique stadiums in the world. Arup
    provided specialist sports architecture and structural engineering
    services for the stadium's bowl design. One of the building's most
    striking features is a facade that changes color from red to white to
    blue, to reflect which home team is playing.

    Architect: Herzog & de Meuron, 2005
    Digital Images © Arup

THE OVERALL TRANSITION
to smart environments
will probably take between
five and 10 years.

Professor Dr. Ludger Hovestadt
CHAIRMAN AND PROFESSOR OF COMPUTER-AIDED ARCHITECTURAL
DESIGN DEPARTMENT, SWISS FEDERAL INSTITUTE OF TECHNOLOGY
ETH ZURICH, SWITZERLAND

The way smart buildings will flourish

HOW MUCH ENERGY COULD AN ORGANISATION SAVE if the heating, air conditioning and power consumption were regulated according to the number of people in the building? How much additional value could building owners generate if they had a more accurate picture of the way their services were being consumed and could charge tenants accordingly? And how much more comfortable would it be to work in a building where smart infrastructure recognised each individual as he or she walked into a room, tailored building services to personal preferences and provided instant access to required IT and communications systems?

THIS IS NOT A VISION for just the long-term future—much of the infrastructure needed to realise it is available today, and other key products will be released in the near future. By embedding Internet technologies into the fabric of a building, deploying inexpensive chip sets and changing the way we manage both electrical and data systems, we believe it is possible to transform the way we interact with our building environment.

There are, of course, many challenges involved in making this kind of transition—from the technical difficulties of creating common user interfaces to the organisational issues associated with managing change in the work environment. The upside, however, is that tackling them will bring enormous benefits for building owners and occupants, both in terms of the quality of the user experience and in overall energy savings. If you can customise the entire work environment to meet the real-time needs of the people working inside, you can replicate those kinds of savings across your whole electrical building infrastructure.

Creating an integrated infrastructure

Every building consists of a multilayer infrastructure. At the first level is the core building framework, which typically has a 50-year life span before it undergoes significant structural change. Within it, the technical infrastructure—including the physical layer of the digital systems and mechanical and electrical systems—is typically renewed on a 10-year basis. At the second level comes the "fit out"—the products and devices that people use to organise their rooms and spaces, which tend to have a minimum life span of two years. The third level is the software and services people use; we classify this level as "zero."

We believe the move to smart buildings will be driven by the home.

The important point about this kind of infrastructure is that each level needs to be embedded in the level below it—so, for example, the software needs to be installed on two-year-lifecycle devices, which in turn connect to the 10-year cabling infrastructure. It is extremely important from an architectural perspective for these levels of infrastructure to be addressed from the very beginning of the design and construction process, so that everything ties together. With this kind of integrated infrastructure, building owners will be able to switch from a function-driven, device-oriented platform to a service-oriented platform—and this significantly increases a building's value by reducing capital and labour, streamlining operational efficiencies and creating personalised building services.

Creating an integrated infrastructure

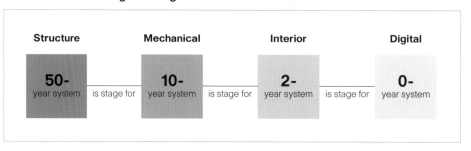

Figure 1 Digital technology is an additional building-systems layer that should be considered early in the planning and design process. Fully integrated communications become the foundation for new applications and services that transform the use and operation of buildings. Source: ETH Zurich, 2006.

Smart-building platform

Services					Network-Integrated Building			
Applications			Internet Building Platform		Internet Communication Platform			
Systems		Life, Safety and Security	Building Automation		Data	Voice	Video	
Devices	Fire-Alarm Control	Security, Video Surveillance, Access Control	HVAC Control	Electricity and Elevators Control	Data Communi-cation	Fax and Text Communi-cation	Voice Communi-cation	TV and Images
	Electrical Technology				**Information Technology**			

Figure 2 The vision of smart buildings becomes reality through the integration of information and electrical technologies over a unified data network. Source: ETH Zurich, 2006. Adapted from Teknibank, DEGW, 1991.

When you compare IT equipment to traditional building devices such as lamps, blinds, elevators, security and access-control systems, there are fundamental performance differences in the speed of development. IT devices, however, perform much better—perhaps by as much as a factor of 10,000 compared to something as basic as a lamp. Yet, in a typical building environment, there will be 10 times as many devices per person that control and manage the building than IT devices per person. This needs to be taken into account by owners when they assess what they should charge for smart-building services. At a minimum, owners should be able to double their investment in each device—traditional building or IT—when they establish a computer-integrated building.

Technology solutions start at home

We believe the move to smart buildings will be driven by the home, not by the office or other commercial buildings, hospitals or public sector buildings. The reasons are simple: high volume is key to lowering the price when it comes to electronics, and residential homes provide the perfect environment for that evolution. Also, residential buildings are the largest market segment, with more space than any other building type, and the needs of home dwellers tend to be generic.

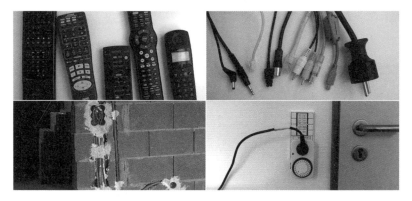

Figure 3 The challenge of integrating digital technology into buildings in the future will be to create user-friendly environments. As shown here, customers struggle with complex cabling infrastructures and deficient user interfaces in traditional buildings. Source: ETH Zurich, 2006.

We face considerable challenges, however, in shifting homes from a traditional to a smart environment. In Germany alone, there are 170 million rooms, 90 per cent of them residential, with more than 1 billion traditional electrical devices installed. We estimate that there are more than 10 billion long-established electrical devices installed worldwide. They use different user interfaces, the cabling on which they rely is based on numerous standards and the sheer volume of electronics required to support something as simple as a light switch is too high. So in order to create a smart building, we need to bring consistency to the user interface and normalise data and communication standards to the Internet.

We estimate that there are more than 10 billion long-established electrical devices installed worldwide.

If we could normalise the control and management of all of these different electrical devices to Internet standards, adding a new device becomes a simple matter of plug and play. In addition, by using the Internet to centralise the control of these electrical devices, we can cut ongoing maintenance costs and improve energy management. For example, €2.5 billion is spent every year in Germany just to keep electrical appliances on standby—for example, a simple TV consumes 20 watts in standby mode. If we could manage each TV set via an Internet-based communications infrastructure, we could cut energy consumption to 0.2 watts. With 1 billion electrical devices installed in Germany alone, this savings translates to €3 billion each year, as well as a significant reduction of greenhouse gas emissions.

To make this possible, we are developing a single chip solution to make all electrical equipment manageable via the existing electrical wiring in buildings. The chip, which will be available in the fourth quarter of 2007, will work on 230V or 110V and 16A devices, translating to 0.2 watts or 0.3 watts standby load for each device. There will also be a universal serial number on the wiring and a digital fingerprint of the energy consumption. The chip would allow users to control devices via an Internet connection consumption so that they can turn devices on and off, switch channels on a TV or radio, open and close window blinds, control individual lights and so on.

Simplified building infrastructure

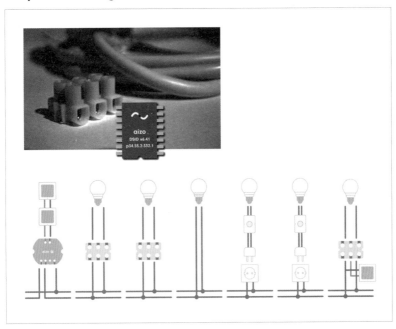

Figure 4 A high-voltage and low-cost chip can be integrated into any electrical device and networked across the existing electrical wiring. Source: ETH Zurich, 2006.

The current building process is one of the major challenges in successfully implementing Internet-based building control and management. Electrical engineering and information-technology engineering are following two different design, procurement and construction paths. By utilising existing electrical wiring as the physical layer for the building control and management infrastructure, electrical engineers are unaffected—there are no new tools to learn, no programming required, no additional training and no extra cabling. This is of particular value to owners of existing buildings, since they can create additional functionality without ripping out existing wiring. In new construction, capital and labour costs are reduced.

In the future, we believe that building owners will adopt two types of nodes in their building-control setups. One is a low-bandwidth node that will manage the lights, motors and other traditional electrical devices, making use of the electrical wiring. The other is a data-centric, high-bandwidth node that is directly connected to Ethernet, perhaps using the Power over Ethernet standard, which eliminates the need for a main power connection and is gaining wide market acceptance. This high-capacity node is for applications such as multimedia data, audio, video, telephone and security cameras.

New buildings, new thinking

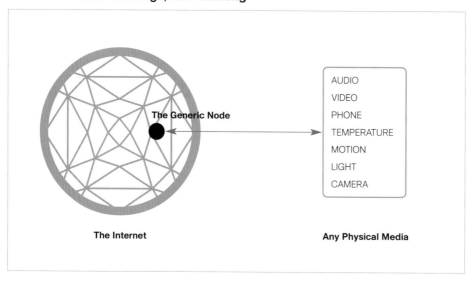

Figure 5 Any physical media at any location in the world can be connected through the Internet by one generic node. Source: ETH Zurich, 2006.

This evolution will transform the way we think about buildings. Today, we tend to think in terms of devices—telephones, TVs, video cameras, light switches or temperature controls—that control our building environment. In a smart building, however, we focus on the network, and devices are simply classified as either "sensors" or "activators." Sensors pick up images, sound or building operations such as cameras, microphones or sensors. Activators react to these inputs— they include speakers to play audio, multifunctional displays to show images and light bulbs and heaters to provide a healthy and comfortable environment. Setting up your digital environment in the form of sensors and activators allows you to organise your devices free from the constraints of hardware. Broken down into its constituent parts, a telephone, for example, consists of a microphone and a digital speaker (which can also be used as an MP3 player or radio), while the "phone" itself is software.

Individuals will be able to turn on the lights, open and close windows and access video through just one device.

Managing the transition to this digital environment requires some care. Even if you break down a telephone into its sensor and activator components, from a management perspective you may still want to make it look like a traditional phone. While trendsetters will want to use the latest technologies, most people are busy and averse to learning new ways of using basic tools—they want devices to behave in the way they always have. They will gradually learn for themselves about the additional capabilities, or they will learn from friends or colleagues who are more interested in exploring the possibilities of digital living.

Over time, some of these functions and services will start to migrate to personal control devices, allowing us to interact with buildings in new ways. For example, individuals will be able to turn on the lights, open and close windows and access video through just one device. Ultimately, these interactions will themselves be automated, and a smart room will be able to recognise every individual who walks in and adjust the environment accordingly. Lighting, for example, may be dimmed to match my personal preferences as I walk into a room, and as my favourite music strikes up, the network will install my personal

65

Perzonalized user interfaces

Ludger Sanjay Dina Chung Kevin

Figure 6 A simple, mobile-user interface—similar to an iPhone—will become the personalized remote control for working, living, playing, learning and building services. Source: ETH Zurich, 2006.

software configuration. At this point, the devices become independent of me—regardless of which TV set or telephone I am near, my personal environment will be re-created automatically. I no longer think about functions in relation to a room—I think about functions in relation to myself.

The operational benefits to the building owner from this approach will be significant. First, they reduce energy costs because heating, ventilation, air conditioning, lighting and other services can be provided on an occupancy basis in which sensors establish who is in the building at any one time. Second, they provide a wealth of real-time building-management information for better decision making. Third, they give owners and building managers access to data about personal energy consumption and use of devices, which makes it easier to charge for services on a demand basis and also to understand infrastructure usage for future planning purposes.

Moving from vision to reality

How quickly will the vision of a smart building become a reality? The key to adopting this concept is the fact that a smart building is built around one generic chip that is mass-produced and, therefore, relatively inexpensive. A smart building requires no new skills for the electrician, and a common interface makes for a comfortable migration path for users, so there is likely to be little resistance to adoption. Early adopters—the trendsetters that make up around 10 per cent of the market—are already looking for this kind of functionality, and we believe they will start to implement it over the next two years. Within five years, we think that there will be a general awareness and acceptance of the difference between a traditional house and a smart house, and the overall transition to smart environments will probably take between five and 10 years.

That represents a major transformation. Today's buildings are managed from a functional perspective; tomorrow's home, office and commercial and public sector buildings will be managed from a services philosophy that creates significant energy savings, operational efficiencies and a far more attractive environment for building occupants.

DR. LUDGER HOVESTADT

CHAIRMAN AND PROFESSOR OF COMPUTER-AIDED ARCHITECTURAL DESIGN (CAAD) DEPARTMENT, SWISS FEDERAL INSTITUTE OF TECHNOLOGY ETH, ZURICH, SWITZERLAND

Dr. Ludger Hovestadt has been a professor for architecture and CAAD at the Swiss Federal Institute of Technology in Zurich since July 1, 2000. He studied architecture at the RWTH Aachen in Germany and the HfG in Vienna, Austria, under Professor Holzbauer. Upon completion of his diploma in 1987, he worked as a scientific researcher with Professors F. Haller and Professor N. Kohler at the Technical University Karlsruhe, Germany, where he received his doctorate in 1994. Between 1997 and 2000, Hovestadt was a visiting professor at the CAAD department at the University of Kaiserslautern in Germany.

Hovestadt's research interests are in the development of design tools and the management of overcomplex systems, with emphasis on generative design, digital production and building intelligence.

THE FOUNDATION of our service-delivery strategy is our network.

James J. Whalen
SENIOR VICE PRESIDENT AND CHIEF INFORMATION OFFICER
BOSTON PROPERTIES, UNITED STATES

Attaining operational excellence

SERVICE EXCELLENCE AND CONSISTENT, STRATEGIC EXECUTION are at the heart of the Boston Properties real estate management philosophy. Our technology investments support these concepts by upholding two core principles: providing broad access to operational information, and positioning the network itself as an enabler of services. The pursuit of these principles strengthens our ability to respond to new business challenges while remaining flexible to the needs of our tenants.

BOSTON PROPERTIES is a self-administered and self-managed real estate investment trust. It is also among the largest owners, managers, and developers of premier office properties in the United States. Our property portfolio is comprised of primarily Class-A office space. Our business model focuses on markets where the barriers to entry are high, and where strong real estate fundamentals limit the increase in competitive supply.

Boston Properties differentiates itself from its peers through its development expertise, seeking complex projects and unique build-to-suit opportunities within our select markets and submarkets. We believe in developing first-class real estate and managing those facilities to become the landlord of choice for both existing and prospective clients. We maintain a significant presence in four core geographical markets: Boston; Washington, D.C.; Midtown Manhattan; and San Francisco. We acquire, develop, and manage our properties through full-service regional offices in these locations, as well as in Princeton, New Jersey.

New network, new strategies

We strive to provide a consistently high standard of service to our 1,500-plus tenants. The depth of our in-house building management and engineering expertise is among the company's core strengths and serves as a foundation for delivering service excellence. Our technology investments allow us to optimize this expertise, and the foundation of our service delivery strategy is our network.

Our disciplined management approach begins with a team of senior management and operational staff in leasing, construction, and property management that collaborates to make investment decisions. Our IT group cultivates partnerships with property management, breaking down traditional barriers to transform the network team into a strategic business resource. Our property management experts recognize IT assets as technology enablers with strategic value. Among real estate owners, this approach is rare. As a result, the partnership between these two groups helps us manage our resources and expenses more proactively. We've interconnected our network from a centralized property management location within a region where we manage an entire portfolio of properties. Centralized management enables us to optimize our staffing resources without sacrificing customer service. By leveraging an array of systems, we maintain an around the clock visibility into each property and extend the coverage of available services beyond normal business hours without the requirement of onsite staff.

Our network allows us to focus on developing and managing an intelligent network of buildings.

In Boston, our flagship operational command center is at the heart of regional building operations, overseeing IT and building-automation systems in over 40 properties throughout the region. A small staff is responsible for a range of duties, such as planned maintenance, response to outages, security monitoring, energy reporting, and response to tenant requests, most of which are made through our Web-based tenant portal. These centralized responsibilities increase the reach and effectiveness of our property managers and their expertise, using wireless technology to communicate with onsite maintenance staff for rapid follow-through. Thanks to these efficiencies, our staff at the Boston command center and other regional management sites handles 150,000-plus tenant requests for service and 80,000 work orders for preventive maintenance each year.

The command center enables a flexible staffing model that complements onsite building technicians with senior engineers who travel between properties. It reduces costs by centralizing the control of building systems and increasing responsiveness to tenant requests 24 hours a day, 7 days a week. The command center also provides reliable, timely responses to tenants with off-hours access requirements.

Operational challenges

Through acquisition and development, Boston Properties has built its portfolio over a period of thirty-seven years. Each new property uses different monitoring and sensor systems. Ideally, property managers could deploy a single set of triggers and events across all systems, but achieving such uniformity is a gradual transition, as legacy systems become fully depreciated and service contracts expire. The numerous building systems require us to manage multiple vendors and proprietary interfaces. The Boston command center manages new and legacy heating, ventilation, and air conditioning (HVAC) systems from five different vendors. The center today relies on banks of separate screens, each dedicated to a single vendor. The operator must match the building with the appropriate system console to respond to a service call.

Truly integrated solutions will take time to develop and mature.

The level of technical sophistication also varies across vendors. One vendor may offer a highly functional Web interface while another may remain grounded in traditional command-line entry. Solutions also differ in terms of their redundancy, reliability, and security. When adding a new solution to the network, we assess each one's potential security risks, which may result in segmenting it from other services.

Truly integrated solutions will take time to develop and mature. The vendor market is responding with new approaches to integration, but mainstream solutions will take a few years to adopt. As we overcome the limitations of multiple proprietary building-automation systems, we rely on a robust set of networking and communications technologies. Our centralized property management system gives us greater visibility into building systems across our properties, including HVAC, building access, security cameras, and parking revenue. Even with these capabilities and successes, however, challenges continue to surface every day.

Energy management is an emerging area of attention for both cost-containment and regulatory compliance reasons. It demands near-real-time access to meter readings instead of monthly utility invoices that cannot enable proactive action. The network helps us efficiently gather data into a single location. For example, it gives us the ability to capture and aggregate near-real-time energy usage from Internet-enabled meters and submeters. We use this data to establish trends for each property.

Extending the network

Boston Properties has extended the reach of its network with technologies appropriate to each situation. For example, a fiber-optic network across five city blocks in downtown San Francisco supports both operational and security-monitoring systems. Across the county in an 18-building campus in Princeton, New Jersey, a wireless network permits HVAC system monitoring and control. In some of our larger properties, fiber-optic loops allow us to monitor cooling towers and connect digital video cameras and recorders remotely.

Energy management is an emerging area of attention for both cost-containment and regulatory compliance reasons.

The network also creates opportunities at new construction sites. For example, the network connected our construction crews and property manager while they developed Seven Cambridge Center in Cambridge, Massachusetts, a new research facility for the Massachusetts Institute of Technology (MIT) that is part of a 2.7-million-square-foot urban center. The development needed a round-the-clock command center for HVAC and security monitoring, including direct voice connections to emergency phones. A wireless network solved the demands of bandwidth and performance with a nine-month payback period. Reaching across the Charles River in Boston, the wireless network connects the seven-building development in the heart of Cambridge with the Prudential Center in Boston and handles an integrated set of services.

These include a new, Internet-enabled garage; Internet devices in parking gates are controlled through new software that manages the entire process, including reporting, sales processing, and capacity management. The end result is a trouble-free and seamless experience for garage users.

In all cases, our flexibility to extend the network infrastructure with a variety of technologies allows us to meet new business needs quickly. A sophisticated set of software tools and devices allows us to manage network security and segment services as needed from the central command center.

Looking ahead

Boston Properties has positioned itself at the top of the class of the commercial-office sector and plans to roll out new services that are consistent with our operating and management philosophies. As with past successes, new services must be based on solid business cases.

As building-automation systems adopt IT standards, they are increasingly converging with traditional IT infrastructures. As Internet technology permeates digital devices throughout buildings, real estate managers can focus on developing creative, cost-effective strategies, enabled by innovative software. The software that intelligently manages a network of these devices will potentially challenge current operating assumptions. Our network allows us to focus on developing and managing an intelligent network of buildings, not just one building at a time. Our essential approach to technology is the belief that connectivity elevates our ability to deliver a sophisticated set of services that complements our philosophy in how we support our tenants and manage our assets—and keeps us on the short list of the most desirable landlords.

JAMES J. WHALEN
SENIOR VICE PRESIDENT AND CHIEF INFORMATION OFFICER, BOSTON PROPERTIES
UNITED STATES

James Whalen serves as senior vice president and chief information officer of Boston Properties, a fully integrated, self-administered, and self-managed real estate investment trust that develops, redevelops, acquires, manages, operates, and owns a diverse portfolio of Class-A office properties in the United States. The company's portfolio is concentrated in four core markets: Boston; Midtown Manhattan; Washington, D.C.; and San Francisco.

Prior to joining the company in March 1998, Whalen served as vice president, information systems, Beacon Properties. He is a graduate of the University of Notre Dame and a recipient of the New York City Urban Fellowship.

1

2

Photography

1 **Embarcadero Center, San Francisco**
A fiber network spans five city blocks of the Embarcadero Center in Downtown San Francisco, supporting both operational and security-monitoring systems.

Architect: John Portman & Associates, 1967
Photo © Sherman Takata, Gensler

2 **Prudential Center, Boston**
The Prudential Center in Boston is the central operational command center for an integrated set of networked IT and building services for the regional real estate portfolio of Boston Properties. A wireless network that reaches across the Charles River to a seven-building development in the heart of Cambridge solves the demand for bandwidth and performance, allowing complete operational control and the remote management of hotel operations and car parking.

Architect: Charles Luckman & Associates, 1964

3 **Times Square Tower, New York**
Built in 2004, Times Square Tower incorporates state-of-the-art facility and security systems.

Architect: Skidmore, Owings & Merrill LLP, 2003
Photo © William Taufic Photography

2 TRANSFORMING WORKPLACES

Organizations are moving from a mindset of "my space" to "team space." Resulting benefits include increased productivity, intensified space usage, and reduced environmental footprint.

THE BEST BUILDINGS of the 21st century will provide ecosystems of spaces that can be fluidly and dynamically occupied rather than being rigid realizations of old-fashioned space-usage programs.

William J. Mitchell
PROFESSOR OF ARCHITECTURE AND MEDIA ARTS AND SCIENCES,
MASSACHUSETTS INSTITUTE OF TECHNOLOGY (MIT), UNITED STATES

The architectural consequences of connectivity

ONE OF THE MOST FUNDAMENTAL, LONG-UNCHALLENGED FOUNDATIONS of architectural theory, practice, and education over the last century has been the idea of the *architectural program*. As I shall argue here, ubiquitous digital interconnectivity challenges this key idea and creates an urgent need for a new approach to framing architectural tasks and developing design responses. This issue can have profound implications, I believe, for 21st-century building designers, developers, owners and managers, and corporate strategists.

The role of the program

Essentially, an architectural program consists of an exhaustive list of the spaces to be accommodated in a building, together with floor areas, environmental requirements, and adjacency and proximity requirements. Programs are often prepared by specialists before architects are engaged, and are conceived of as specifications of client requirements. In the early stages of design, architects transform programs into diagrammatic floor-plan layouts and massing concepts that satisfy these requirements as closely as possible. Through the stages of schematic design and design development, architects take care to retain consistency with these early space-allocation diagrams. Finally, the program is used to verify that the architect actually met the client's needs, and to establish a starting point for occupancy planning and facility management. The program is a crucial control device.

All this seems eminently reasonable, but it depends on some underlying assumptions that are increasingly questionable in an era of digital interconnectivity. Far greater architectural and management benefits can be realized by critically departing from these assumptions and exploiting the new design opportunities this enables than by simply networking traditionally programmed buildings and filling them with electronic devices.

Fluid versus rigid space use

The most fundamental assumption of the traditional architectural program is that of stable space use. A program makes sense only if it is assumed that spaces have much the same uses over time, and should therefore be optimized for those uses. Private office spaces are different from meeting rooms or social spaces—with different area, environmental, and adjacency requirements—and are designed in response to those differences.

Furthermore, under traditional assumptions, moving and conversion costs exert an additional stabilizing effect. If you have lots of books and paper files, moving from one office to another is time-consuming, costly, and disruptive; you don't do it lightly. Conversion of, say, conference rooms into offices in response to changed space demands is slow and expensive, and removes the space from usable inventory while the conversion takes place.

One effect of networking and mobile electronics is the elimination of the need for spatial separation.

Under these conditions, circulation efficiency within a building tends to degrade over time—a process much like fragmentation of a computer's hard-disk space. The initial layout may be carefully organized to minimize unnecessary circulation, but patterns of demand gradually change, and some of the initially programmed uses change so that the assumptions on which the layout was based no longer hold. Because of moving and conversion costs, however, it is not realistic to keep adjusting the layout to maintain efficiency as this happens. There is no equivalent to running a utility to clean up your computer's disk space.

Probably the most important effect is the creation of new synergies among activities.

But, where work is supported by ubiquitous connectivity and portable and mobile devices, the use of space can become much more fluid. Anywhere you can sit down with a network-connected laptop, or use your cell phone, becomes a potential workspace. Where work materials and tools are stored in portable memory, or delivered via the network, moving costs are reduced to almost zero; to change offices, you simply pick up your laptop and go. And, with temporary space occupancy and negligible moving costs, readjustment of proximities is quick, easy, and continual; if you need to be adjacent to someone, you just walk over and sit down for a while.

Overall, buildings for the mobile, networked era need a few, very broad categories of space defined by basic human needs rather than by many, highly differentiated categories. And, like locations in computer memory, locations within these spaces are assigned based on use and then immediately freed up for other needs. The consequences of this, if it is effectively managed, are higher duty cycles (the proportion of time during which a component, device, or system is operated) for spaces, more efficient use of available spaces, and better operating efficiency. Spaces that would otherwise be assigned as private offices don't have to be vacant while their occupants are in meeting spaces, for example, and inefficient layouts don't have to be maintained because they are too slow, difficult, and costly to change.

Multiplexing space

A second assumption now in question is that users spend lengthy chunks of time in particular activities at specific locations (individual work in offices, meeting in conference rooms, eating in cafeterias, and so on), and circulate from space to space as activities change. The motivation for this highly generalized allocation of time, in traditional work environments, is obvious. If building users switched activities too frequently and sliced their time too finely, they would be running from space to space continually, and they would never get anything done.

A related factor is the traditional incompatibility of certain activities. Quiet work and noisy music are incompatible, and a traditional architectural response is to locate them in separate spaces. The same is true when it comes to eating and drinking in a library; librarians, concerned about book preservation, don't like to see food and drink occupying the same space as books.

One effect of networking and mobile electronics is the elimination of many of these incompatibilities and, consequently, the need for spatial separation. In the age of the iPod, you can have music and quiet work in adjacent seats. And, in the age of electronic delivery of text to laptop screens, you can read a book at a cafeteria table without worrying about getting ketchup on the pages.

A second effect is the possibility of electronically switching among activities, at a rapid pace, without physically moving. Switching from doing your e-mail to attending a meeting to relaxing no longer requires you to go from your office cubicle to a conference room to a recreation space. You can simply go, via your computer screen, from an e-mail browser to a videoconferencing session to a music player. The transition costs are now negligible, so you can slice time as finely as you want.

Fine time slicing shades imperceptibly into multitasking. For instance, if you keep several windows on your computer screen open at once, you can rotate your attention among them, or keep an eye on several at once—an impossible strategy if even minimal physical movement from space to space intervenes.

Probably the most important effect, though, is the creation of new synergies among activities. Traditionally, for example, group meetings and consultation of technical references in the library have been separate activities, conducted in separate spaces at different times. But, when meeting participants have wireless laptops, they can instantly search a topic when it comes up in discussion, and then inject the results back into the discourse. Multitasking creates a new, flexible, and powerful way of pursuing and debating ideas.

Human versus technological space

It is often assumed that advanced, electronically serviced workspaces—as suggested by the examples in this essay—must look and feel high tech. In fact, precisely the opposite is true; advanced technology tends to disappear into your pocket, via a PDA, or into the "woodwork," and makes few demands on the workspace architecture. Instead of responding to technological imperatives, this technology can respond to basic human needs for light, air, view, and sociability.

Multitasking creates a new, flexible, and powerful way of pursuing and debating ideas.

In the recent past, for example, telephones were part of the architecture—attached to walls or desks. Now, phones have become extensions of our mobile bodies. Within some pretty broad limits, technological imperatives no longer determine where you can conduct the activity of telephoning. At the same time, though, mobile telephony has created an even greater need for environments that provide the socially desirable options of speech privacy and freedom from auditory disturbance wherever you may need it—as, for example, in the addition of "silent cars" to trains.

Similarly, audiovisual presentations were once conducted in darkened rooms, with the secondary consequence that presentation spaces often were located in the interiors of buildings where there wasn't any natural light. Today's high-powered video projectors and large, flat-screen monitors can operate effectively in rooms with high levels of natural light. Meeting rooms can now be designed—in a far more humane way—in response to the basic human desire for light, air, and view.

Computers used to be delicate beasts that required precise climate control. Environments dominated by these machines' requirements were horrible for human beings, but there was no other option. Today, you can use laptops safely in far less-controlled environments that are designed around the needs and desires of people. You can even take them outside, under a tree, to work on a beautiful spring day.

We can create large-scale buildings that are nonrepetitive and sensitively responsive to their contexts, and to the basic human desire for varied and interesting environments.

Finally, the large-scale buildings of the industrial era—and, ironically, those of Silicon Valley and Massachusetts Route 128 —were modular and repetitive. This was because, in order to meet pressing budget and schedule requirements, architects invariably had to trade complexity for the economies of scale that resulted from one-size-fits-all strategies. But, through the use of three-dimensional digital modeling in design, combined with digital fabrication and mass-customization strategies in building production, it is now possible to readjust radically the parameters of this trade-off. Through reasonable timeframes and budgets, we can create large-scale buildings that are nonrepetitive and sensitively responsive to their contexts, and to the basic human desire for varied and interesting environments.

Paradoxically, the best buildings of the 21st century will incorporate their advanced technology unobtrusively, and will have more in common with preindustrial buildings than their industrial-era predecessors. They will be highly varied; permeable to light, air, and view rather than tightly sealed off; and will provide ecosystems of spaces that can be fluidly and dynamically occupied rather than being rigid realizations of old-fashioned space-usage programs.

Real-time space markets and management

Under conditions of fluid, dynamic, ad-hoc space occupancy in a building, a space market begins to operate. The building's managers are space providers, the occupants are space consumers, and the task is to match supply to demand effectively on a minute-by-minute basis. This is a potentially demanding task.

It is easy to imagine working in a large building and wandering around—increasingly frustrated—looking for a place to sit down and work. It would be much like searching for a space in a crowded airport parking structure. But there is a solution: mobile connectivity. A simple system, for example, might employ sensor technology to keep track of currently unoccupied desks and, via mobile devices, direct new arrivals to them. More sophisticated systems might perform complex tasks such as arranging meeting spaces at the nearest available locations, conducting eBay-style auctions for highly desirable spaces, or implementing congestion pricing for space in the most popular locations. Organizations could take advantage of the distributed intelligence and self-interest of building users, and create powerful incentives to use their space effectively and efficiently.

There are many markets that would benefit from mobile connectivity. The hospitality industry in regard to hotel rooms has many transactions, with time constants of days, and it is sometimes useful to have real-time availability information. Space markets for street parking have a great many transactions, and time constants of hours or minutes. They often require drivers to search onerously for a parking spot, so real-time availability information would be great if you could get it. Future workspaces will probably operate as dynamic space markets, with transactions conducted at a rapid pace and mobile, networked devices playing an essential role in connecting users to available spaces that best meet their current needs.

How connectivity adds value

Commercial and industrial real-estate development is largely a game of adding value to land by intensifying its use. New technologies have always played a crucial role in this. High-rise construction technologies—particularly the steel frame, the curtain wall, and the elevator—enabled development of skyscrapers in the Chicago Loop, Manhattan, and other urban cores. Electric light allowed much more effective use of buildings after dark. Air conditioning opened up sites in hot climates to more intensive development. And, as described above, digital networking has an additional intensifying effect. Few systematic studies of this have been carried out so far (and they are sorely needed), but it seems clear that effectively managed networked workspaces should achieve higher densities of occupants per unit floor area, and higher duty cycles for spaces.

For building managers, higher densities and duty cycles should translate into reduced space inventories and greater capacity to respond to organizational growth and change without inventory expansion. Since rising energy costs produce increased space costs, economizing on square footage is even more important than it has been in the past.

More important, well-managed networked space should reduce traditional rigidities in spatial organization and minimize barriers to effective intercommunication and collaboration. Space that is fluidly occupied and allows effective multitasking is more able to respond effectively to rapidly changing needs and conditions, generating benefits from synergistic groupings and overlays of activities. And space that is humanized through reduced dependence on old-fashioned technology should provide higher levels of user satisfaction.[1]

Commercial and industrial real-estate development is largely a game of adding value to land by intensifying its use.

For developers, these benefits potentially translate into higher rents. But it is not automatic. It is necessary to make the design and management moves that are required to realize the potential benefits, to rethink traditional metrics—for example, calculations of net-to-gross ratios and rentable areas—for the new conditions, and to make the justifying arguments effectively to potential renters.

The cost of integrating networking with new construction is generally marginal, so it makes no sense not to do it.[2] It can, however, be surprisingly difficult and expensive to retrofit older buildings with wiring closets and vertical and horizontal wiring distribution space, and

---

1. The usual way to measure user satisfaction is through questionnaire surveys. In work settings, it is often better to measure productivity rather than satisfaction. This is more objective and closer to what owners and managers care about.

2. The capital investment for a building information network is approximately 2 percent of the construction costs. Bandwidth Now, 2006.

this must be factored into decisions about the future of older building stock. On the other hand, adding good networking technology can be a crucial factor in the successful, adaptive reuse of historic structures; it is unobtrusive, but it opens up new use possibilities.

In general, compelling economic logic can be expected to drive the transition to highly networked spaces and related new patterns of space use. Under most circumstances, the benefits (from the perspectives of both real estate developers and building occupants and managers) are high and the costs are low.

What will it look like?

Who can say? The future of architectural expression has never been predictable. But I can, at least, suggest one interesting starting point for thinking about this. Programmable surfaces, such as large light-emitting diode displays and various forms of "electronic paper," are rapidly diminishing in cost. Eventually, they will be comparable in cost to many more traditional architectural surfaces, such as curtain walls. At that point, there will be no practical barrier to making the external faces of buildings as dynamic as the patterns of use within, or to instant personalization of interior spaces according to current occupancy.[3]

Perhaps this will make cultural sense, and we will see an architecture of programmed iconography rather than fixed expression, as author, teacher, and architect Robert Venturi has long suggested. Perhaps the old slogan "form follows function" will take on a new, dynamic, network-era meaning.

WILLIAM J. MITCHELL

PROFESSOR OF ARCHITECTURE AND MEDIA ARTS AND SCIENCES, MASSACHUSETTS INSTITUTE OF TECHNOLOGY (MIT), UNITED STATES

William J. Mitchell, professor of Architecture and Media Arts and Sciences at MIT, holds the Alexander W. Dreyfoos, Jr. Professorship. He is also the director of the MIT Design Laboratory. He previously served as dean of the School of Architecture and Planning at MIT, and as architectural advisor to MIT's president.

Mitchell is also an author. His most recent book is *Placing Words: Symbols, Space, and the City*. From 2002–2003, he chaired the National Academies of Science and Engineering panel, which produced the report *Beyond Productivity: Information Technology, Innovation, and Creativity*.

3. Some of the best examples are the Agbar Tower, Barcelona; the Kunsthaus, Graz; the SPOTS installation, Berlin's Potsdamer Platz; the Galleria Fashion Mall, Seoul; and the Chanel building, Tokyo.

1

2

3

4

Photography

1 **The Stata Center**
The Stata Center (shown here as a model) at the Massachusetts Institute of Technology, in Cambridge, Massachusetts, is home to the Computer Science and Artificial Intelligence Laboratory, the Laboratory for Information Systems, and the Department of Linguistics and Philosophy. Its striking design—featuring tilting towers, angular walls, and whimsical shapes—challenges the conventional wisdom of laboratory and campus-building designs.

Architect: Gehry Partners, 2002

2 **The Student Street**
The Student Street at the Stata Center at the Massachusetts Institute of Technology, is a continuation of Stata Center's infinite corridor system. The Student Street is a place in and of itself. Its various nooks and crannies offer students spaces to socialize, work in an informal setting, or escape with a good book.

Architect: Gehry Partners, 2002

3 **The Stata Center Grounds**
The well-landscaped grounds of the Stata Center at the Massachusetts Institute of Technology, invite informal gatherings.

Architect: Gehry Partners, 2002

4 **BIX Facade for the Kunsthaus Graz**
The BIX facade is a permanent light and media installation for the new Kunsthaus, a biomorphic building structure in Graz, Austria. BIX is a matrix of 930 fluorescent lamps integrated into the eastern Plexiglas facade of the Kunsthaus. The Kunsthaus' outer layer transforms into a giant low-resolution computer display on which films and animations can be displayed. (www.bix.at)

Media Installation: realities:united, 2003
Architect: Spacelab Cook-Fournier, 2003

THE DEMAND from our employees for flexible working arrangements and related technology allows us to approach space in new ways.

Mark Nicholls
CORPORATE WORKPLACE EXECUTIVE, BANK OF AMERICA, UNITED STATES

Banking on tomorrow's workplace

TODAY'S CORPORATE WORKPLACE differs radically from that of yesteryear, and tomorrow's can seem unimaginable.

My job is to imagine it.

Put simply, any company that fails to anticipate and address the evolving needs and desires of its workplace associates and customers will not be competitive.

In this essay, I highlight some of the workplace concepts we have incorporated at Bank of America to maximize our real estate investment. More broadly, I describe our workplace philosophy, which is designed to foster productivity and satisfaction among our wonderfully diverse global team. Our approach is driven by the knowledge that strategic evolution benefits all of our stakeholders: associates, customers, shareholders, and, as a result, our corporation itself.

Improving our corporate workplace organization

There are three fundamental, internal variables within our kind of organization: people, process, and technology. We have recently analyzed each in order to improve our real-estate management practices.

We first studied the overall talent mix within our organization, based on assessments of each individual relative to world-class standards.

Then we assessed the technology-support systems and asked ourselves: Do our associates have standard desktop platforms? Do they proficiently use their systems' full capacity? Do they have flat-screen monitors that are easier on the eyes and lead to better productivity? What core systems are in place to extract and manipulate data?

Finally, we analyzed the processes and asked, for example: How many approvals are required to secure a capital budget request? And what factors are considered when deciding whether to invest in a pair of US$2 million projects rather than one US$4 million initiative?

Each of these areas was then assessed on a simple 10-point scale—where we were that day and where we wanted to be, taking into account factors such as customer and associate requests and corporate objectives. It proved a difficult exercise, given that all three areas are critical to our business. But it was vital to rank them and identify the largest challenges. In my experience—and I do not think it differs in many organizations—the most significant gap usually is in people, followed by process, and then technology.

Having established the priorities, we set out to create a new role for a corporate workplace executive: a senior position to rank alongside the executives who support our different businesses. (Bank of America is structured along three lines of business, each run by a general manager who reports to the chairman.) We recruited three people to fill the corporate workplace executive role in each of those business units and also created a fourth executive role to work with the bank's three corporate staff functions, which cover risk, human resources, and finance.

Having established the priorities, we set out to create a new role for a corporate workplace executive.

It is important to stress that the corporate workplace executive is a strategic role; as one of three units in a US$72 billion organization, each line of business is a major operation in its own right, and our executives are, in effect, general managers representing the corporate workplace organization. Our focus is on execution—rather than selling ideas to the general manager of each unit, our role is to understand their requirements and provide solutions to their specific challenges. We thus conducted a lengthy research process to establish priorities and pain points, and mapped out single-page service-level agreements with the president of each unit to define solution deliveries. Those agreements contained goals, objectives, expectations, and routines.

We also instituted a Workplace Research & Development Council, a function dedicated to researching industry trends and best practices, benchmarking, internal marketing, and developing educational and change-management programs to support our workplace strategies. The Council comprises strategic leaders drawn from both the corporate workplace and external service providers.

This obviously is an ongoing process—our business is large and complex, with 9,000 facilities and more than 90 million square feet of real estate in 37 countries. But these institutional changes have allowed us to enjoy significant progress in anticipating and addressing evolving workplace needs.

Focusing on the green

In a very tangible sense, we are fortunate that our next generation of associates often questions assumptions about the way we work. With tens of thousands of potential associates seeking to join our 200,000-plus employees worldwide every year, workplace is a significant competitive differentiator for us.

Some of the macro issues our associates care about—such as our organization's impact on the environment—are written into our corporate DNA. "Doing the Right Thing" is one of our enunciated core values, and we have an ingrained appreciation for our impact on and responsibility toward the environment. We are building the second-tallest skyscraper in Manhattan, the 52-story Bank of America Tower at One Bryant Park, where we have committed to achieve platinum LEED (Leadership in Energy and Environmental Design) Green Building System certification, which is a voluntary national standard for developing high-performance, sustainable buildings. When Bank of America Tower opens in 2008, it will be the first high-rise office building in the world to attain that environmental standard.

It is our intention to continue to pursue the viability of sustainable design or LEED certification on all new projects we undertake. Our real-estate practices can positively influence our impact on the environment, and we are committed to making all of our facilities as environmentally sound as possible.

Exploring space

Significant evidence indicates that the design and use of our workplaces directly and significantly influence associate productivity and customer satisfaction. In 2001, we engaged in a comprehensive survey of our customers and were surprised by the weight they placed on the quality of the retail bank environment. They naturally were concerned about practical and safety issues—they wanted ATM vestibules to be well lighted at night, and they wanted prominent, bright signs easily visible to drivers—but their concerns went further. They cared about potholes in the parking lot and clearly delineated lines between parking spaces.

And it mattered to them if the carpets were frayed when they walked into a branch.

These issues seem obvious in retrospect, but at the time were important findings. Such insights drive ongoing and future investment; our customers need safe ATM vestibules and well-maintained branches, so we spend capital to deliver them.

Empty offices during working hours echo with the sound of coins rattling up the air vents.

The importance of workplace design, however, also implicates our goal of maximizing the return on investments already made—specifically, using our space more effectively. Industry benchmarking studies indicate that the utilization rate for corporate office space typically is anemic, at best. Most associates are working 40 or 50 hours each week, with significant time spent in meetings, training, or at client sites. Factor in several weeks of vacation and sick days, and it becomes clear why office utilization rates sometimes dip as low as 14 percent—compared to a minimum generally acceptable level of around 70 percent for alternative capital investments in manufacturing.

In short, empty offices during working hours echo with the sound of coins rattling up the air vents—capital investment that could more profitably be directed elsewhere.

Taking work to the workers

Interestingly, a confluence of socioeconomic factors appears to be resolving the conundrum of empty office space: today's associates are technologically sophisticated and averse to spatial work limitations.

Recent college graduates have been conversant with personal computers since they were young—these are tools rather than a revelation. As a result, there are expectations about the quality of the IT equipment provided, as well as a willingness to rely on technologies to support new manners of working.

Furthermore, a large portion of our new hires (and long-time associates for that matter) expects more flexibility in where, when, and how they work. Gone are the days when every associate arrived at his or her individual cubicle at 8 a.m. and left at 5 p.m. This demand for flexible working arrangements and related technology allows us to approach "space," and how we define space efficiency, in new ways.

Similarly, there has been a clear shift in perceptions among the younger generation about the relationship between where they live and work. There has been a resurgence in downtown living and a growing resistance to commuting, attributable to factors such as time compression, gasoline prices and insurance, and environmental concerns. This sea change, in turn, is transforming the way we, as a corporation, think about work.

For more than a century, economies have depended upon transporting large numbers of workers to factories, plants, and other capital-equipment sites in order to build goods. Today, for jobs that rely on intellectual capital, it is a corporation's responsibility to bring the work to the associates.

This clearly is a complex equation. The solution is not simply to encourage working at home, since our internal data suggests that people are not inclined to work there exclusively. Instead, the solution comprises a combination of locales—home, as well as a local branch, for example, rather than headquarters. We have introduced a flexible work program, titled My Work, which addresses these needs and fosters increased productivity. Under the program, associates exchange dedicated workspace for the flexibility to work from home, satellite offices, drop-in centers, or any location that proves viable. The My Work pilot celebrated its one-year anniversary in 2006, and is being expanded to include additional sites and lines of business.

We will continue to explore ways of increasing both associate productivity and satisfaction, measured by enterprisewide and line-of-business-specific surveys and studies, while putting our real estate to more efficient use. Someday soon, we will no longer suffer shockingly low space utilization compared with the efficient operations inherent in competitive economies, such as those of India.

Measuring success

If the organizational structure provides the platform for achieving our objectives, our workplace metrics are critical to understanding our performance and maximizing value. At a strategic level, our Workplace Strategy Oversight Committee plays a vital role in shaping our planning. The committee, comprising about half of the corporation's top 12 executives, meets on a quarterly basis to analyze internal and industrywide real estate benchmarking data about our existing position and direction, with the goal of instituting world-class practices.

As a corporation, we are not as interested in establishing targets for five and 10 years out—there are too many variables to make such a practice meaningful, and we are already mapping next year through our financial-planning processes. Rather, we are focused on two to three years out. The committee thus provides feedback on our assessment of where we should aim to be in that time period, which provides the framework for problem solving and execution.

The metrics we use include several standard measures, such as the number of square feet per full-time employee and the cost per square foot. Where we differ perhaps from other organizations is that we do not seek solely to reduce these ratios. There are, for example, instances where we add space to align with business-unit goals and provide associates with a more productive working environment.

Ready for tomorrow, today

We continue to transform our practices and structure in order to remain ahead of workplace trends and maintain our considerable productivity. But every alteration is attributable to our unchanging goal of becoming the global bank of choice, and the world's most admired company, through doing things the right way.

What will our corporate workplace look like in generations to come? You can only imagine.

MARK S. NICHOLLS

CORPORATE WORKPLACE EXECUTIVE, BANK OF AMERICA, UNITED STATES

Mark S. Nicholls is corporate workplace executive for Bank of America, where he is responsible for developing workplace strategies and real estate strategies, covering over 97 million square feet of space for the company's 177,000 associates. He also manages a US$3.8 billion expense and capital budget.

Nicholls joined the bank in May 2001 as personnel executive for Transaction Services. Until assuming his current role in September 2004, Nicholls was senior personnel executive for the Technology & Operations, Quality & Productivity, and Legal lines of business.

Before joining Bank of America, Nicholls held various leadership roles at Honeywell, and its predecessors, for eight years.

Nicholls received a bachelor's degree in business and organization development from Bowling Green University in Ohio, and a master's degree in business administration from the University of Georgia. He is currently an executive board member of Jobs for America's Graduates and participates on the Real Estate Executive Board.

My Work

Description:

- My Work is a flexible work program that enables associates to work in ways they can be most productive. It introduces the idea that work is an activity, not a place.

- Associates are not assigned any workstation or office, and have the ability to work in a variety of places. They are 100 percent flexible, and can easily work anywhere, anytime.

- J. Steele Alphin, chief administrative officer for Bank of America, and the human resources team piloted this program beginning in July 2006.

- The program is currently expanding into Charlotte, North Carolina, and to more lines of businesses. We are also opening more sites.

Impact:

Competitive Advantage

- Promotes agility.
- Increases productivity and speed.
- Differentiates Bank of America.
- Attracts and retains talent.

Associate Satisfaction

- Reduces commute time.
- Allows flexibility in where and when to work.
- Makes better use of time.
- Improves work/life balance.

Cost-Efficiency

- Reduces real-estate costs.
- Lowers operating costs.
- Increases profitability.

Bank of America Tower,
One Bryant Park, New York City

Description:

- Bank of America Tower will rise 945 feet above the west side of Sixth Avenue between 42nd Street and 43rd Street. The building will serve as headquarters for Bank of America's operations in New York, housing primarily trading operations, its Global Corporate and Investment Banking businesses, and its Wealth and Investment Management businesses.

Impact:

- Upon completion in 2008, the US$1 billion project will result in the world's most environmentally responsible office building, focusing on sustainable sites, energy and the atmosphere, water efficiency, and indoor environmental quality.

- It will be the first high-rise office building to strive for the U.S. Green Building Council's Leadership in Energy & Environmental Design (LEED) platinum designation.

- The building will offer an enhanced associate experience: higher ceilings and translucent insulating glass in floor-to-ceiling windows permit maximum daylight in interior spaces, optimal views, and energy efficiency; under-floor displacement air ventilation system and floor-by-floor air-handling units allow for individual floor control and more even, efficient, and healthy heating and cooling; carbon dioxide monitors automatically adjust the amount of fresh air when necessary; air-filtration systems remove 95 percent of particulates as air enters the building.

- Energy consumption is reduced by a minimum of 50 percent.

- Potable water consumption is reduced by 50 percent.

- Storm water contribution is reduced by 95 percent

- Obtained 50 percent of building material within 500 miles of site.

1

Bank of America Tower
Upon completion in 2008, the Bank of America Tower at One Bryant Park in Manhattan will be one of the world's most connected and environmentally responsible office buildings.

Architect: Cook+Fox, 2004
Developer: The Durst Organization

To PROVIDE a more pleasant, open environment that encourages internal collaboration and teamwork, we need technologies that allow people to share information within the same building and remotely.

José Ramón Burgos
HEAD OF CORPORATE REAL ESTATE, REPSOL YPF, SPAIN

The role of the workplace in achieving strategic business goals

REPSOL YPF IS UNDERGOING A PERIOD OF MAJOR CHANGE. The opening of two new corporate offices in Madrid, Spain and Buenos Aires, Argentina has prompted a wide-ranging review of the way we work—and simultaneously, of the way we use our space. By the time the new buildings are opened in the fourth quarter of 2008, we expect to have created a very different physical environment for our employees, encouraging new, collaborative working methods and introducing remote working for the first time.

BASED IN MADRID, REPSOL YPF IS AN INTEGRATED, INTERNATIONAL OIL AND GAS COMPANY operating in more than 30 countries, and the industry leader in Spain and Argentina. We have 35,000 employees distributed across 20 countries worldwide. We made a decision several years ago to relocate our two headquarters and build two new corporate offices. In 2004, we launched an extensive initiative to understand how our usage of building space affects the way we work. We are planning to use the new buildings as the template for all of our new-building initiatives around the world.

This is a huge undertaking, and we have been under no illusions about what it involves. Successful execution depends on winning the buy-in of employees at every level of the company. It also requires close collaboration among multiple business functions—including the corporate real-estate team, human resources, IT and Repsol's senior management—and among the different participants in the design and construction process. Not only are we constructing two new corporate buildings; in effect, we are also rebuilding our internal culture—and technology is a key enabler in this process.

From managing space to managing people

When I joined Repsol as corporate real estate director in 2005 and took charge of the two building projects, initial construction had already started. At that stage, however, very little space planning had been carried out. We decided to launch a comprehensive planning and research initiative, with two objectives in mind. First, we needed to make the real-estate operation as cost-effective as possible; this meant optimising the way we use the new space, as well as using the building as a trigger for introducing more efficient and effective working practices. Second, we set out to ensure that the project would play a significant role in improving employee satisfaction. While the main focus of my department is to manage the buildings and associated services, the ultimate goal is to create an innovative environment that stimulates cultural change to provide a better working life for Repsol's employees.

Our aim is to provide a more pleasant, open environment that encourages internal collaboration and working in teams while enhancing employee satisfaction.

From a design perspective, the key to improving our space usage lies in reducing the amount of square footage dedicated to individual employees. Today, Repsol's buildings are laid out along traditional lines, with desks and offices allocated to named individuals and an implicit hierarchy in the way larger offices are assigned. Our plan is to cut the amount of fixed office space as much as possible. We will use the available space to create more open, collaborative spaces. Today, dedicated cubes stretch from wall to wall. In our new buildings, the dedicated spaces will be along the interior, with collaborative spaces around the perimeter.

This open space will allow us to provide a range of new services for employees. We will build lounges for informal meetings, dedicated areas for think tanks and in-house cafeterias. These are new concepts for Repsol, and they will transform the work environment. Our aim is to provide a more pleasant, open environment that encourages internal collaboration and working in teams—and at the same time enhances employee satisfaction.

We are also investigating whether we can make further reductions to our fixed space through remote working. When I first joined Repsol, nobody worked away from the office. As we started to liaise more closely with the human resources teams, however, we discovered that attitudes were changing. We have consulted extensively with our workforce to get an understanding of perceptions at every level of the company. I was impressed with how open the company can be to innovative ways of working. We are now researching three likely scenarios for the new buildings—a traditional work environment where 100 per cent of the space is assigned; a less conservative setup, where about 50 per cent is assigned; and an innovative workplace environment where approximately a quarter of the space is assigned to specific employees.

We have made the decision to allocate space according to the needs of different kinds of users. We group people into four loose categories to define the way they work. Managers, for example, are typically referred to as "helicopters"—they consume relatively little space because they travel a lot, dropping into the office for informal and formal meetings. At the same time, they often require more technologies such as mobile devices, laptops and videoconferencing. Other typologies include networkers, process-oriented professionals and engineers and technical professionals.

The importance of change management

We know that the changes we are envisaging have enormous implications at every level of the organisation, and there is a concerted effort under way within the company to raise awareness of the different possibilities. We need people to understand that in order to realise the full potential of the new corporate offices, some cultural change is inevitable. We fully appreciate, for example, that space is associated with status—if you are a director, you are accustomed to working in an office of a certain size. But we need to break that connection—it is not an effective use of space, and, frankly, it is not a democratic practice for a modern company. So it is very important to explain what is happening, encourage feedback and "sell" the new concepts. This is a long change-management process that, for a project of this scale, starts at least a year in advance of a building's opening.

We have already begun this consultative work at a senior level. Over the course of two or three months, we surveyed about 50 directors and other managers in detail, explaining our plans and asking for feedback. The response was very positive. Respondents cited a range of factors that they were seeking from our building services, including

103

better knowledge exchange (21 mentions), improved teamwork (17 mentions), the ability to adapt rapidly to change (15 mentions) and better motivation through a greater focus on work-life balance (11 mentions). We believe that the first two requirements—knowledge exchange and teamwork—will be aided by the new, collaborative layout, while new service concepts such as lounges and cafeterias should be important employee motivators. The ability to change rapidly will be a feature of the modern building design.

Collaboration among multiple business functions

The decision-making process throughout the project has been highly collaborative. Once the corporate real-estate team has completed our analysis of space usage, we will liaise with the human resources managing director, possibly bring in external experts, and set up a change committee. We already have a project committee in place consisting of the main business divisions that are helping to drive the project forward, including human resources, IT, security, health and safety and corporate communications. Each of these functions plays a critical role in taking the project forward, particularly human resources and IT. Human resources, of course, is responsible for managing organisational change and for smoothing the transition from Repsol's actual position to its more modern positioning as an innovator. The changes that we are discussing—from the way people work and interact in the office to the gradual adoption of remote working— represent an enormous cultural shift and have significant implications across the company.

We know that the changes we are envisaging have enormous implications at every level of the organisation.

IT is also a critically important partner. In most building projects, the technology team tends to get involved after the construction work has been completed. This lack of consultation up front can severely limit the value IT can deliver. We believe, however, that technology is one of the key enablers to making cultural change possible. If we are to improve collaboration, we need technologies that allow people to share information and work on joint projects, both within the same building and remotely. Likewise, as we start to embrace teleworking, we need to ensure that our employees stay connected from their different locations. This means wireless technologies, videoconferencing and other capabilities must be built into the design and planning phases. We have been working with IT for more than a year on the new project, and have taken an inclusive, integrated approach from the very beginning. We hold regular meetings covering all aspects of IT, from systems to core infrastructure technology.

A collaborative design and construction approach

This collaborative approach extends to building design and construction. We hired Foster & Partners, led by Lord Norman Foster, as the principal architect. His office is involved in multiple phases of the project. On Foster's recommendation, we also brought in steel and concrete consultants, and we now have a number of experts on board from the United States, Argentina, Germany, Spain and Britain, including space-planning specialists. Similarly, we worked with Pelli Clarke Pelli Architects, led by Cesar Pelli, on our project in Buenos Aires.

If we are to improve collaboration, we need technologies that allow people to share information and work on joint projects, both within the same building and remotely.

Managing a high volume of third-party suppliers and service providers can get complicated, from both an operational perspective and as it relates to our changing business-needs definition. This year, for example, there have been legislative changes in Spain regarding the building code, and a new energy law is coming into force—both of which will affect our plans for a "green" building. Given this complexity and the different regional requirements, we were reluctant to have operational management of the two projects handled centrally—with projects of this size carried out on different sides of the world, the risks are high. We, therefore, have two project managers—one in Madrid and one in Buenos Aires—who take responsibility for preparing tenders, hiring general contractors, overseeing the different subcontractors, managing costs and safety, and so forth. The teams meet with the central corporate real-estate team every week, and once a month provide detailed reports on all aspects of our progress.

Changing corporate culture

While it will be two years before our construction work is completed, its impact is already being felt throughout the organisation. As the construction takes shape, we expect to see further cultural change seep through the company. As an industry, we have long known that collaborative environments and effective space utilisation can have a major impact on streamlining our real-estate investments. What we are setting out to prove at Repsol YPF is that if we are supported by connectivity and collaborative technologies, we can also transform working practices and corporate culture.

JOSÉ RAMÓN BURGOS

HEAD OF CORPORATE REAL ESTATE, REPSOL YPF, SPAIN

José Ramón Burgos is head of Corporate Real Estate for the Spanish oil company REPSOL YPF, which he joined in 2005. He is responsible for the company's land, buildings, construction, maintenance and facilities management. Current projects include two new corporate headquarter towers, which are under construction in Madrid and Buenos Aires.

Burgos has 30 years of experience in construction and development, both in Europe and in North America. He was building director for one of Spain's largest contractors, Agroman, and prior to joining Repsol, he was operations director for Bovis Lend Lease, where he was responsible for more than 30 simultaneous projects throughout Spain, including the US$646 million (€500 million) Telefonica Business Park.

Burgos studied civil engineering at the Universidad Politécnica in Madrid.

1

Torre Repsol

The new headquarters building for Repsol YPF oil and gas company is located in the Cuatro Torres Business Area in Madrid, Spain. Upon completion in 2008, Torre Repsol signals the company's commitment to exploring alternative energy sources. The top of the building is designed to incorporate wind turbines, which are capable of providing a significant proportion of the building's power supply.

Architect: Foster + Partners, 2002–2008

IN A WORLD where people are increasingly mobile, physical presence counts more than ever.

Mark Dixon
CHIEF EXECUTIVE OFFICER, REGUS GROUP PLC, UNITED KINGDOM

Work without boundaries

IF YOU WERE DESIGNING A RESIDENTIAL NEIGHBOURHOOD TODAY and wanted to cater to residents who expect more flexibility in where and how they work, what would you add to the traditional development mix? High-speed communications and the IT infrastructure required for remote-working environments are a given, of course. But what about adding a business centre at the heart of the community? Connected to all of the houses in the area, a business centre could provide a central hub where people could hold client meetings and access copying resources and other specialist services—and also interact with their neighbours over coffee or lunch.

IN A WORLD WHERE PEOPLE ARE INCREASINGLY MOBILE, physical presence counts more than ever. The ability to provide social interaction for employees away from the corporate office is a significant business benefit. According to Tony Venables, economist at the London School of Economics, face-to-face communications count for a growing share of economic activities.[1]

At Regus Group, we have been researching and addressing evolving workplace needs in response to growing organisational change for many years.[2] As a shortage of skills starts to bite in the coming decade and companies battle to acquire and retain knowledge workers, we believe that providing a flexible work environment will be as important as delivering a competitive pay package and a stimulating job. Some employees will want to work from a neighbourhood office near

---

1. From the article "Press the Flesh, Not the Keyboard," *The Economist*, August, 2002.

2. Virginia Gibson, *The New Agenda: Rethinking Corporate Real Estate in the Face of Growing Organizational Change* (Regus 2006).

where they live, rather than endure a long commute to reach the corporate campus; some will want to stay connected while collaborating with clients and employees remotely; and others will want to work from home on a part-time or even full-time basis (see Figure 1).

Technology and the impact on organizations

DRIVER	FOCUS	IMPACT
• Technological Innovation and Change	• Quality Improvement	• Organizational Restructuring
	• Cost Reduction	• Changing Modes of Production
	• Globalization	• Process Improvements
		• Product Diversification
		• Changing Relationships Between Firms
		• New Location Choices

Figure 1 Source: Virginia Gibson, *The New Agenda: Rethinking Corporate Real Estate in the Face of Growing Organizational Change*, The Regus Group plc, August 2006.

Providing this kind of flexibility presents a huge challenge to most organisations, given their limited experience in managing office space, services and technology infrastructures. In their recent article "Corporate Relocation and Economic Development: Future of Work," Charlie Grantham and James Ware, co-founders of the Work Design Collaborative and the Future of Work programme, made the following analysis: "In today's dynamic global economy, organisations are compelled to move away from a fixed-cost structure to variable-cost models in order to reduce capital requirements and risk, while simultaneously increasing their agility and responsiveness to changing environments. This new reality, in combination with equally dramatic changes in work-force demographics, means there is a powerful need for closer integration between corporate real estate operations and community-based economic development initiatives." [3]

3. Charles Grantham and James Ware, *Location Strategies: Where Do You Need to Be?*, CoreNet Global, July 2006.

There is a powerful need for closer integration between corporate real estate operations and community-based economic development initiatives.

These shifting work patterns are already being reflected in the changing mix of the Regus Group's business. Well known as a provider of managed and serviced office space, we provide flexible office and training facilities through 750 locations in 60 countries, housing everything from corporate headquarters and branch offices to one-person businesses. At the same time, we are building a network of drop-in centres for people in transition, from wireless "Laptop Lanes" at airports to railway stations and town-centre locations. In addition, we now provide services directly to people who are mobile and work remotely, whether they are employees of large companies who travel to the office a couple of days a week, or entrepreneurs launching a new business from their spare bedroom. As well as providing a sophisticated technology and communications infrastructure, we offer a host of office services to these customers (see Figure 2).

Where work gets done in 2010

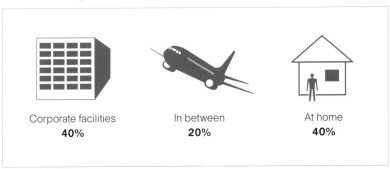

Corporate facilities	In between	At home
40%	**20%**	**40%**

Figure 2 Source: Work Design Collaborative, CoreNet Global, 2005.

This shift toward mobility is taking place on a huge scale—in fact, at Regus we are on our way to supporting more people working remotely—from both home and the road—than from our offices. Going forward, we believe that the ability to meet this changing demand will be critical to business success, as workplace flexibility becomes a differentiator in global competition for talent.

Shifting demographics

There is little doubt that the nature of the work environment is changing.[4] A shortage of skills is a growing problem in most of the developed world, and even in some emerging economies, driven in part by declining birth rates, which will continue to slow the overall growth of the workforce. This raises the stakes in the competition for talent, and means that organisations will need to become creative in order to attract and retain the most valuable employees.

Mobility and business agility are driving the need for increased portfolio flexibility.

At the same time, workforce requirements are changing. The fastest-growing workforce category is self-employed workers[5] —people who, in many cases, work from where they live, whether it be part time or full time. Older workers are also tending to stay in their jobs longer, with many of them looking for part-time opportunities and flexible hours. Similarly, the U.S. Bureau of Labor Statistics predicts a more than 20 per cent increase in the number of professional and related jobs between 2004 and 2014, particularly in areas of computing, healthcare and education.[6] This represents a major shift toward "knowledge work," which will have a significant impact on our working practices—because by its very nature, knowledge work is not tied to any specific location. Assuming that they have a suitable technology and communications infrastructure, knowledge workers can operate from remote locations as effectively as they would in an office.

The next generation of our workforce is already embracing this philosophy. Young people are far more wired technologically than before, and simply cannot see the point of travelling vast distances in order to use office PCs, telephones, faxes and copiers when they can use their own resources at home. Brought up with video games and other electronic media, they are comfortable with the concept of working with technology on their own, and can do so in any environment.

---

4. Richard Florida, *The Flight of the Creative Class: The New Global Competition for Talent*, (Harper Collins, New York, 2005).

5. *Corporate Real Estate 2010—The Changing Nature of Work and the Workplace*, CoreNet Global Inc., 2005.

6. "Tomorrow's Jobs," *Occupational Outlook Handbook*, U.S. Department of Labor, Bureau of Labor Statistics, 2005.

These changing dynamics will alter the work landscape dramatically by bringing the relationship between living and working closer together. While big cities will remain important metropolitan hubs—the rebirth of downtown living is one indicator of this trend—we believe regional workplaces will become an increasingly important part of the business location equation. According to a recent report, *Corporate Real Estate 2010—The Changing Nature of Work and the Workplace*, by CoreNet Global, Inc., work will increasingly be carried out in a wide range of locations. "People will gravitate to physical locations that best support the exact work they need to do. And these locations will not be in the same building, or perhaps even the same city—they will be wherever in the world the work needs to be done..."[7] Many organisations are starting to recognise that the need for this kind of flexibility is affecting the corporate real estate portfolio strategy of organisations. Mobility and business agility are driving the need for increased portfolio flexibility (see Figure 3).

The core/peripheral corporate real estate portfolio

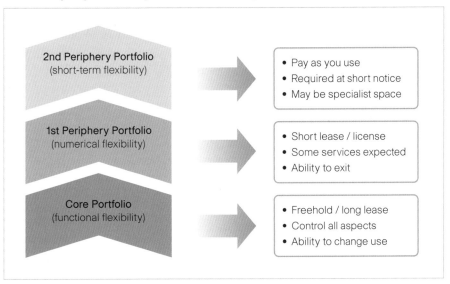

Figure 3 Corporate real estate portfolios are structured with increasing flexibility. Source: Virginia Gibson, *The New Agenda: Rethinking Corporate Real Estate in the Face of Growing Organizational Change*, CoreNet Global, Inc., 2005.

7. Virginia Gibson, *Corporate Real Estate 2010—The Changing Nature of Work and the Workplace*, CoreNet Global, Inc., 2005.

Historically, mobile working has often been seen as a way of saving money in property overhead, as opposed to a strategic business advantage. Those who prefer to work remotely—whether full time, part time, or by alternating their working locations—will be more inclined to stay with an employer that offers workplace flexibility rather than with a rival that insists on them coming to the office five days a week. Knowledge industries—such as pharmaceuticals and some information-technology sectors—that face an acute shortage of skills are already aware of this, and some of our leading customers now market their flexible work facilities as a key component of their employee packages. Over time, providing a work environment that meets employees' needs will be critical to acquiring and retaining the right people.

We help companies tackle the biggest challenge of mobile working: the lack of social interaction.

While employee retention is important, the shift to mobile working offers other direct benefits to employers. For one thing, it can improve productivity. In an office environment, it is very easy for people to hold unnecessary meetings, attended by employees who have only a marginal interest in the issues. When people work from different locations, holding a meeting means travelling distances—and they will do so only if they are convinced it is worth their time. Similarly, people who work remotely may experience fewer distractions—fewer people stopping by their desks to chat or have informal discussions, for example. The growth of instant-messaging technologies may counteract some of these advantages, but it is generally easier to shut a virtual office door than to find peace in a crowded office. This trend is

Mobile workers in the United States, 2004 and 2008 (in millions)

2004	44
2008	51

Note: people who regularly work from home on at least a part-time basis

Figure 4 Source: In-Stat/MDR and eMarketer.com, 2004.

supported by market research from In-Stat,[8] which shows that in 2004 about 30 per cent of the total U.S. workforce—44 million employees— were remote workers, and that mobility will become more available to a growing percentage of the workforce by 2008 (see Figure 4).

Managing the transition

While the benefits—and the growing business imperative—of providing a more flexible work environment are becoming apparent, managing this kind of change presents several major challenges. To begin with, many organisations lack the necessary experience to manage a distributed workforce, and their working practices are built around the assumption that the bulk of their employees will be in one place at the same time. If they want to hold a meeting, they expect to do it in a conference room; if they want a one-to-one conversation, they expect to do it at their desk. Similarly, managers sometimes struggle with the concept of supervising direct reports who aren't in the same building.

There are also challenges from the employee perspective. People feed off one another to develop ideas, and many of the more creative aspects of work, such as collaboration and brainstorming, rely on physical togetherness. Many employees also struggle to separate their work and personal lives. Ironically, while managers often worry that mobile workers' productivity will drop, the problem is often the reverse—once people are connected remotely, they tend to find it hard to shut off reading and sending e-mails late at night when they should be resting. So the transition requires a lot of training and education.

Many organisations also fail to provide suitable support. Some companies think it is enough to provide an employee with a laptop computer and a broadband connection and to help pay their telephone bill. But if the focus is purely on infrastructure and helping with expenses, mobile working is little more than a cost-cutting exercise and employees can be left feeling isolated (see Figure 5).

Regus is developing a Personal Assistant-style service for workers; if they need research to be carried out or want to have something typed, our central service centre or a local centre will handle it for them. We also manage basic services, from stationery to couriers—in some countries, it can be quite difficult to set up an account with a shipping company, so we handle that centrally. These kinds of services provide practical support and also generate softer

8. Source: www.instat.com, July 2004.

Remote-working business issues

Major business benefits and obstacles to implementing remote working, 2004	
Benefits	**Obstacles**
Reduced real estate overhead	Management of remote workers
Improved worker productivity	Security of networks
Better work/life balance	Lack of equipment or technology
Employee retention/attraction	Reduced sense of team camaraderie
Better customer service through flexible work location and hours	Threat to corporate culture and management style
Business continuity in times of disaster	Loneliness and isolation for the remote worker
Less commuting: less pollution	Ocupational health and safety responsibilities

Figure 5 In-Stat/MDR, and eMarketer, 2004.

benefits—if employees feel their company is taking steps to guarantee they have the services they need, it helps create a positive perception.

We also provide portable telephone numbers and addresses: instead of employees using their home telephone and having material sent directly to them, our central service fields and forwards calls and routes correspondence. This is an important safeguard for employees; it means their remote-office contact details can easily be switched to the company.

Above all, we are able to help companies tackle the biggest challenge of mobile working: the lack of social interaction. Not only are people working on their own—they may also be using the telephone less than they used to, as e-mail and instant-messaging technologies gradually reduce the requirement for voice conversations. Our locations provide a place for employees to interface with their colleagues. We have lounges at every centre, providing a productive place to work, as well as in-house coffee houses, child-care facilities and a range of community activities. Whether you are talking to people from your own company or from elsewhere is academic—it is the ability to chat, bounce ideas around, and remove the feeling of isolation that matters. On a practical note, the centres also provide a back-up facility: for example, if you have contractors in your home, or your children are home for the holidays, or you have simply gone stir-crazy, the centre offers a refuge.

116

Our centres can be considered "third places," a concept developed by urban sociologist Ray Oldenburg. In his book *The Great Good Place*, Oldenburg emphasises the importance of society's "third places."[9] These are informal community settings where residents enjoy social interaction and shared environments in addition to their traditional family and workplace settings—their first and second places. The success of these "third places" depends on their physical location—just as people might walk three blocks but not four to find a coffee house, we are expanding our network of business centres to ensure that we are in the near vicinity of where most of our mobile employees work, live, play and learn.

Tying the vision together

Providing services that keep corporations and their employees in touch with each other requires two core capabilities: a technology and communications infrastructure that keeps corporations connected, and the ability to provide office- and community-related services across multiple environments.

We think of buildings with technology as one combined solution. Unconnected buildings are pieces of concrete and mechanical equipment, and of no use to anyone.

The technology itself works on two levels. At an infrastructure level, the hardware and communications capabilities are integrated into the building infrastructure. We think of buildings with technology as one combined solution. It is pointless to have a building without your basic hardware and connectivity. Unconnected buildings really aren't buildings at all; they're pieces of concrete and mechanical equipment, and of no use to anyone. So internal and external connectivity capabilities are built into the fabric of each of our offices, and organisations with their own IT department can run their IT solutions on top of our framework. In the mobile environment, we wire people up and then provide communications, such as voice over Internet and software-based videoconferencing.

9. Ray Oldenburg, *The Great Good Place* (New York: Marlowe & Company, August 1999).

Running across this backbone, we have also invested in software that ties together the different parts of the organisation. The software provides visibility into individual employees' locations so that businesses can communicate effectively with them, along with data on the services they are consuming. We do not manage that consumption —we provide data on it, so companies can manage it themselves. In effect, mobile workers become their own self-contained profit and loss entities, running their own part of the business with associated costs.

Because of the complexity of providing these services, we believe that the outsourcing model will become more common over time.

Logically, there is no reason companies—in particular small and medium-sized ones—would want to be involved in the real estate business; many of them aren't operating their workplace environments cost-effectively. Worse, it can be a distraction from their core business, which is where their management efforts should be directed. Ultimately, what companies are looking for are secure places where people can collaborate and do their work, with the flexibility to change their setup to meet their shifting business requirements. This is what a workplace service provider offers.

Whether it is a one-man operation, a 10,000-employee corporation, or a network of people working from home, our job is to tie these different components together efficiently and productively. In this new workplace landscape, we no longer view buildings, technology and people management as separate issues—rather, they are interrelated to provide a combined work environment solution that employees need, the productivity gains that companies seek and the economic development communities desire.

Work environments are no longer a sole real estate issue—they are becoming a strategic business issue for organisations. Work without boundaries—supporting people to work wherever, whenever and however they choose—defines a competitive advantage in the global competition for talent in an increasingly connected, innovative and flexible business environment.

MARK DIXON

CHIEF EXECUTIVE OFFICER, REGUS GROUP PLC, UNITED KINGDOM

Mark Dixon, chief executive and founder of Regus Group plc, is one of Europe's best-known entrepreneurs. Since founding Regus in Brussels, Belgium in 1989, he has achieved an impressive reputation for leadership and innovation. Prior to Regus, Dixon established businesses in the retail and wholesale food industry. He is the recipient of several awards for enterprise, and has revolutionised the way businesses approach their property needs with his vision of the future of work.

Nokia Case Study

In industries where products and technology are continually evolving, time-to-market is critical for maintaining a competitive and financial advantage. To help in this business environment, Nokia's corporate real estate department undertook an initiative to become more flexible and responsive to the needs of the enterprise by re-evaluating its real estate portfolio management approach. Nokia divided its portfolio into three segments based on the size and type of usage of the real estate being occupied:

- **Small—typically up to 20,000 square feet and 100 people**
  The strategic approach for the small segment is that it can be cut or shrunk at a moment's notice. This segment utilises a unique approach of a "pay as you go" leasing model with a fixed global and tiered pricing and service structure. Nokia teamed up with Regus on a worldwide basis rather than multiple individual lease contracts. Additionally, set-up costs for the small segment are kept to a minimum for better flexibility. Sixty per cent of Nokia's offices, by number, are project offices, which primarily constitute this small segment.

- **Medium—up to 100,000 square feet and 500 people**
  The approach for the medium segment is retaining a degree of flexibility, while at the same time aligning with the business strategy. Most offices in this segment are supporting R&D programs and, as a result, the lease terms are normally three to five years. The medium segment typically comprises R&D centres and country hubs.

- **Large—over 100,000 square feet and 500 people**
  The strategic approach behind the large segment is for long-term stability and consolidation. Manufacturing facilities and regional corporate offices make up this large segment.

Source: *Corporate Real Estate 2010 Research*, CoreNet Global, 2005.

For more information, see "Delivering World-Class Workplaces: Corporate Real Estate Leader," *Journal of Corporate Real Estate*, *2001*, T. Venable, Mark Tamburro, and the Nokia Team, Vol. 3 (2), 39–43, March 2004.

THE OFFICE BUILDING is no longer a stable building type. While still accommodating office work, offices are likely to become multiuse, accommodating many other activities.

Dr. Frank Duffy
FOUNDER, DEGW PLC, UNITED KINGDOM

Justifying place in a virtual world

IMAGINE AN ENTIRELY VIRTUAL WORLD populated by virtual beings that enjoy all the power and convenience of virtuality. One day a virtual genius within this virtual paradise lights upon the notion of physical place. What arguments would this virtual being need to muster to defy the conventions of virtuality and persuade his or her fellows that real places—physical space as well as virtual space—should complement and enhance the self-evident benefits of virtuality?

ARCHITECTS ARE NOT PARTICULARLY VIRTUAL BEINGS. Addicted to physicality, we adore whatever is concrete—structures, materials, places, things. We tend to underestimate abstract ideas. We take our roles as place-makers and constructors for granted. In office design, particularly in the English-speaking world, we have become integral to the remorseless logic of a long-established supply chain that leads from investors and pension funds, through developers, real estate brokers, and corporate real estate practitioners, to tenants, facilities managers, furniture manufacturers, and other suppliers—and ultimately to Scott Adams' cartoon character, Dilbert, and his hapless colleagues trapped in a bureaucratic maze, abandoned to their fate in an endless, windowless landscape of office cubicles.

This has not always been the case. Just over 100 years ago, architects in Chicago and New York invented the 20th-century city through an imaginative appreciation of the massive changes that were then sweeping through the American economy. They had an equally imaginative grasp of new constructional technologies—steel frames, curtain walls, elevators, and new environmental services—and of new delivery-process development, brokerage, and space planning. This energetic and all-embracing vision, the complete opposite of a passive response to change, generated enormous wealth by creating new building types—notably the high-rise office—to accommodate what were then novel work processes, new office technologies, and an entirely unprecedented work culture. Even 30 years ago, American office buildings still impressed Europeans with their technological superiority, architectural magnificence, and sophisticated management of design, construction, and facilities. This is no longer the case.

At the mill with slaves

Far too much is taken for granted by architects, and not just those in the United States. Not enough questions are being asked. Yet paradoxically, we are living in a period in which technological and social change has never been faster or more far-reaching.

What are these changes? In the early days of the Industrial Revolution, 200 years ago, when the ancient agrarian way of life—based on a very different calendar of seasons and saints' days—was being superseded, country folk found their way from the hills and fields into mills in the valleys. There they were captured by the twin imperatives of synchrony and co-location: two new and entirely necessary conditions for getting work done, given the limited technology of the time, and the need to work together at the same time, in the same place.[1]

We need to go back to first principles to design workplaces and ways of using cities that are appropriate to the emerging technology, economy, and work culture of the 21st century.

Today, the social implications of technological change are very different but even more pressing. And yet, the increasingly anachronistic logic of the Industrial Revolution continues to be taken for granted in office design. In this changing context, the vast majority of contemporary offices are not good enough—and are getting worse.

Hence the need for a null hypothesis, at least one that is as strong and sweeping as the one illustrated by the imaginary virtual world sketched above, in which the enormous potential of virtuality is

1. William J. Mitchell, *City of Bits: Space, Place and the Infobahn,* (Cambridge MA: MIT Press, 1995).

expressed in a deliberately exaggerated form in order to challenge inherited assumptions about the nature of time and place. Temporal and spatial conventions do not invent themselves. They are cultural constructs for which we are all responsible. Architects in particular have a new opportunity to justify their existence. We need to start again from nothing, going back to first principles to design workplaces and ways of using cities that are appropriate to the emerging technology, economy, and work culture of the 21st century. The only way to reinvent the workplace and, ultimately, the city is to reject outmoded formulae.

A legacy

The realisation that the office building may not continue as a stable building type for much longer, and certainly not in its present form, may be a necessary contribution to the rediscovery of "place to business" in an increasingly virtual world. Understanding how the office has developed in response to technological change is the key to comprehending how knowledge work should be accommodated in an increasingly virtual future.

The history of the office over the last hundred years can be condensed drastically into three main phases:

- The rise of what should be termed the Taylorist Office after Frederick Taylor, the highly influential proponent of "Scientific Management."[2] Deeply influenced by explosive growth and consequent scarcity of labour in the American economy after the Civil War, Taylor's genius in the context of manual work in heavy industry, taken up later with enormous ingenuity and vigour by Henry Ford, was to sideline conventional craft skills in favour of a much more top-down and rigorous "scientific" approach in which the judgement and skill of autonomous craftsmen were replaced by centralised measurement and top-down control. Scientific management was as influential in the office as it was in industry. The pursuit of greater efficiency and more complete managerial control rapidly found architectural expression in strictly uniform grids to accelerate construction; in enclosure to emphasise hierarchal differences; and in highly standardised, open-plan office layouts to facilitate supervision.

2. Siegfried Giedion, *Mechanization Takes Command*, (Oxford University Press, 1948).

The worldwide and continuing success of this North American model
of office design throughout much of the 20th century
and into the 21st century owes much to Taylor's inspiration.

- The first big exception to the dominant North American model of
  the office was the Northern European reaction in the 1960s. After
  a decade of experiments in Büerolandschaft ("office landscape")
  offices to combine higher environmental standards with
  cybernetically influenced open-plan layouts, the dominant trend
  in Northern Europe shifted sharply in the early 1970s[3] toward
  what might be called the Social Democratic office,
  which was not characterised by efficiency but rather by the
  opposite (for example, by establishing the right of all office
  workers of whatever rank to their own individual office rooms).
  Such rooms were designed on democratic principles to be the
  same size; to give everyone external aspect and views; to be
  naturally lighted and ventilated; and to be equipped with easily
  rearranged and ergonomic, domestic-style furniture. The process
  by which these offices were procured was as democratic as their
  layout, involving user representatives and, eventually by statute,
  workers' councils. It was not long before established standards
  found their way into building regulations as statutory norms.

- The emerging model of office design is what might be called the
  "networked office" (see Figure 1), the physical consequence of
  rapid development in distributed intelligence in the two decades
  since the legitimisation of the personal computer by IBM in
  the early 1980s. The first wave of physical impact was evident
  internally with the computer having escaped from the computer
  room, finding its way down the corridor into every corner
  of the office. The second wave was more about mobility on
  an intercontinental scale, leading to the rapid globalisation of
  certain industries—the first of which was financial services, with
  huge consequences for the economy of cities such as London.
  The third wave was the discovery by other kinds of enterprises,
  which all realised very quickly that time and space could be
  used globally, 24 hours a day, seven days a week, in much more
  continuous and productive ways. This was led by the IT providers

3. Francis Duffy, *The Changing Workplace* (Phaidon Press, 1992).

themselves, then by the global consultancies, and finally by knowledge-based enterprises such as the oil companies and the pharmaceutical giants. The fourth wave has been smaller enterprises, and even individuals, learning that they, too, could work in the same highly mobile but virtually interconnected ways.

The networked office

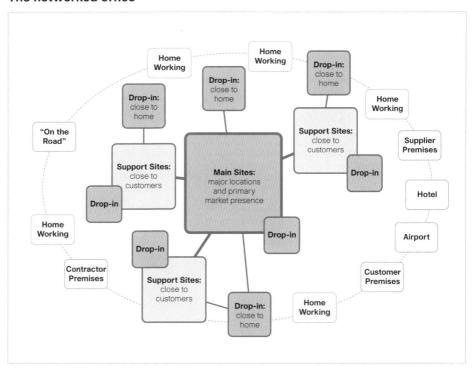

Figure 1 The Networked Office is the emerging model of 21st-century office design. This workplace strategy accommodates a fluid series of customer relationships, office workers, and suppliers distributed over space and time in multiple locations. Source: Frank Duffy, 2006.

From an architectural point of view, the consequences of the networked office are far-reaching. Office design is no longer shaped by fixed relationships between groups of office workers located in particular buildings in predetermined places. Instead, office design now has to accommodate a much more subtle and fluid series of relationships distributed over space and time in multiple locations (some owned, some not), chasing unpredictable patterns of occupancy, all of which are temporary. Hence the phenomenon of the distributed workplace, which can be distinguished from both Taylorist and Social Democratic Offices not just by unprecedented spontaneity and instability, but by totally novel conceptions of the use of time as well as space.

A century of failed scientific endeavour

A plausible argument could be made that distributed working is likely to diminish the importance of the physical working environment for business; working environments that are temporary and unpredictable may not be as critical to occupants' well-being as environments that are fixed and permanently occupied.

The problem with this hypothesis is that not only is it hard to test on its own terms, but also that we know so little about the wider question of the impact of offices on any sort on business performance. The shocking fact is that almost 100 years of scientific enquiry into the relationship between office design and business performance has produced few replicable results of any practical value. There are practical reasons for the general failure to establish a robust empirical basis to evaluate the design of offices, even of the most conventional kind:

- The inherently complex and multivariate nature of the relationship, even at a single point of time, between the working environment and business processes, organisational structures, and corporate cultures.

- The volatile commercial and economic context within which businesses operate.

- The large-scale, longitudinal, and multilayered nature of the physical working environment.

- The clumsy, fragmented, and largely feedback-free way in which the office supply chain is managed.

- The rapid rate at which office organisations and office technology are changing and developing compared with the sluggish pace at which office buildings are planned, procured, erected, and refitted.

- The plural and highly political nature not only of businesses, which by definition are directed and purposeful, but also of office buildings and interiors, which are used variously by different constituencies to express their culture and values.

Given such a wide canvas of constituencies and interests, and the huge variety of physical and temporal scales within which businesses operate, it is not surprising that conventional social science methods haven't worked. They have excluded too many variables, and they have relied too much on data from individual respondents rather than from the businesses as a whole. Perversely and pointlessly, in business, social, and environmental contexts that are all about purpose, most such studies have aspired to be value-free.

We are at the frontiers of scientific endeavour.[4] Measuring the relationship between the working environment and business performance is possible, but only under certain conditions. Successful performance is never predetermined since it depends firstly on the clarity with which managerial purpose is prioritised and communicated; secondly on how skilfully office workers are involved, so that they become committed to achieving the goals that have been set; thirdly on how rigorously the contribution of design to facilitating the achievement of business goals is measured; and fourthly on the recognition that business purposes and priorities inevitably change. The relationship between design and business performance depends on context. Even more important, the relationship can never be regarded as value-free; it is inherently political.

Powers of design

Recent experience of working with rapidly changing businesses in both the public and private sectors—in Europe as well as in North America and Asia Pacific—has made it possible to reframe research questions about what design can offer office organisations in a much more powerful way.

Buildings are inert. Admittedly, in relatively rare and extreme conditions, offices can harm the human beings who work in them—sick building syndrome is a notorious example. On their own, office environments do no good. Office environments used within a wider business framework, however, have the potential to be used to facilitate the achievement of certain business goals. Consequently, in relation to business purpose, the performance of the working environment can, thus, be measured—not in the abstract, but within specific contexts in terms of its contribution to the achievement of three levels of business objectives, which in DEGW are called the three "Es":

4. John Zeisel, *Inquiry by Design* (W.W. Norton & Company, 2006).

- **Greater efficiency**—cutting occupancy costs and other business costs—for example, fewer and cheaper square meters of office space per employee per year. Office space is an expensive resource but is often grotesquely underused, especially over time. A clever manager can cut costs and drive up the productivity of space use, especially using wireless technology to encourage increased mobility internally and externally.

- **Enhanced effectiveness**—using design to add to business performance—for example, not just cutting costs but providing the conditions under which management can create positive value. Locating attractive meeting places in the right locations can help support interdepartmental interaction. Providing safe, ergonomic workplaces can help attract and retain valuable staff. Lively, interesting environments can help stimulate creative people.

- **More consistent and powerful expression**—using design to communicate business values to specific audiences externally and internally. The design of the workplace can be used internally to broadcast powerful messages to staff about how much certain patterns of behaviour—openness, accessibility, collaboration— are valued. Externally, individual office buildings can be powerful statements of corporate values. Across continents, the way space is allocated is an important means of maintaining cultural consistency within organisations.

Such measures can be used to set targets for the contribution of design to business performance. Both targets and measures, of course, must be expressed operationally in specific contexts, in the same terms— a powerful and practical way of connecting office design with business purpose.

The very fact that office design is now frequently integrated with deliberate attempts on the part of management to change organisational culture has two huge implications for architects. The first is that both the briefing and design processes can be much more actively engaged with stimulating change; that is, briefing becomes an essentially *catalytic* process, deliberately creating the conditions for change. The second is that such active engagement on the part of architects creates the need for much greater ethical responsibility in at least two senses: (1) architects must decide whether they agree with the client's aspirations and act accordingly, and (2) architects must take responsibility for measuring whether the client's aspirations have been met and, if not, establishing with the client the reasons for failure and acting accordingly. Responsibility itself may be regarded as a kind of ethical feedback loop.

The contribution of place

To return to our virtual beings: what arguments must our virtual genius muster to persuade his or her fellows that real places should complement and enhance the convenience of virtuality?

The first part of the answer lies in the paradoxical growth in popularity of cities in an increasingly wired-up economy. We live in an urban age where, for the first time in history, the majority of the world's population lives in cities. Within the wider phenomenon of urbanisation, and taking a strictly knowledge-management perspective, the real value of cities is that they constitute concentrations of knowledge, communicated in a partly physical and partly virtual way through multiple, overlapping networks.

Within the wider phenomenon of urbanisation, the real value of cities is that they constitute concentrations of knowledge, communicated in a partly physical and partly virtual way through multiple, overlapping networks.

For example, mapping the way in which professions work—say, in London and New York—provides cartographic insight into the complex social and intellectual matrices of law, medicine, engineering, or architecture. What makes these professions relevant to this discussion is that they are both pre- and post-Taylorist in their operations; they are more networked, more social, more interdependent, and far more permeable within and between themselves than typical corporate enterprises. Furthermore, some professional practices are large; most are tiny. Such practices are independent and highly competitive, but they take constant collaboration across business boundaries for granted. They operate fluidly and from multiple locations, depending on finely calculated serendipity to maintain open-ended contacts—in the government courts or operating theatres, lecture halls, and clubs. Professionals work in their own offices and homes but also work socially in restaurants and coffee houses, and even on busy streets—much as cities operated in the 18th century.

Office buildings in their conventional forms, whether Taylorist or Social Democratic, are much more limited and limiting as infrastructure models of 21st-century ways of working. Taylorist offices are too biased toward top-down control. Social Democratic offices are too slanted toward individual comfort and isolation instead of encouraging the open-ended, collective discourse that is the mark of the knowledge economy.

Consequently, the second part of the answer to the question about the relevance of place is to be discovered in the increasingly mobile patterns of work being adopted by millions of people equipped with powerful, portable communications devices. As work spills out into the street, into homes, and into cafes, restaurants, hotel lobbies, and airport lounges, the networked office transcends individual office buildings. Wireless campuses in university cities such as Cambridge, Massachusetts in the United States—where students have already become extremely skilled at using multiple environments to link their complex, knowledge-based lives—are prototypes of the manner in which the networked office will be used. The corollary, stated earlier, is that the office building is probably no longer a stable building type. While still accommodating office work, offices are likely to become multiuse, accommodating many other activities.

As work spills out into the street, into homes, and into cafes, restaurants, hotel lobbies, and airport lounges, the networked office transcends individual office buildings.

What both cities and networked offices must continue to provide is serendipity, nonlinearity, and chance, as well as meaning, memory, and association—a rich, complex language that will always be attractive because such qualities transcend more elementary forms of communication. Open-ended discourse in cities and networked offices will neither be contradicted nor replaced, but rather enhanced by the accessibility of electronic networks. Concentration of access to people and knowledge of every kind is what will make distributed ways of working successful.

Our virtual genius would probably understand such a vision of the distributed workplace. But in two decades, so changed will be our vision of work and the workplace that most ordinary humans, as well as all virtual beings, are likely to have difficulty understanding what a conventional 20th-century office building was meant to be.

DR. FRANCIS DUFFY

FOUNDER DEGW PLC, UNITED KINGDOM

Dr. Frank Duffy founded the DEGW partnership with John Worthington and Luigi Giffone in 1973. DEGW has offices in Amsterdam, Glasgow, London, Madrid, Melbourne, Milan, New York, Paris, and Sydney. Dr. Duffy was chairman of DEGW from 1989 to 1999 and now works from DEGW's London office.

Dr. Duffy has spent his career helping businesses use space more effectively over time, and he is particularly interested in change management and in measuring how effectively and efficiently buildings are being used to meet clients' changing goals. His work at DEGW falls into three main categories: relating changes in organisational structures and information technology to office and other kinds of design, developing DEGW research, and developing the theory and practice of design through writing theoretical and research papers and technical information books for architects.

He is a past president of the Royal Institute of British Architects and of the Architects' Council of Europe. Dr. Duffy was an elected architect member of the U.K. Architects Registration Board from 1996 to 2002 and is a trustee of the Architecture Foundation. He was made a commander of the British Empire in 1997, and in 2004, he received the President's Award for lifetime achievement from the British Council of Offices.

Dr. Duffy trained as an architect at the Architectural Association School in London and was a graduate student at the University of California at Berkeley and at Princeton University. He developed an interest in organisation theory and in the design of office buildings when he was a Harkness Fellow of the Commonwealth Fund in the United States in 1967 and 1970.

1

2

3

4

Photography / Images

1 **Reliance Building, Chicago**
The Reliance Building in Chicago is one of the first examples of a new type of building—the high-rise building. Completed in 1895 and 202 feet tall, the Reliance Building accommodated new work processes, new office technologies, and an unprecedented work culture.

Architect: Burnham & Root, 1895

2 **Viennese Coffee House**
The club is essentially an ingenious early 19th-century device to allow the kind of people who are now called networkers to share as supportive an environment as possible. It originated in the more ad hoc associations formed in the coffee houses of large cities.

3 **The Larkin Building, Buffalo**
The Larkin Building in Buffalo, U.S., is an example of the rise of the Taylorist Office in the early 20th century.

Architect: Frank Lloyd Wright, 1904

4 **Union Carbide Building, New York**
The Union Carbide Building is an example of the North American tradition of the Taylorist office design at its height in the mid-20th century: Efficient space planning, interior design, and equipment to improve the productivity of office workers were considered integral parts of work processes.

Architect: Skidmore, Owings, and Merrill, 1960

5 **The Genzyme Center Atrium, Cambridge, Massachusetts**
The Genzyme Center combines innovative design and cutting-edge technology to create an exciting collaborative workplace for employees, and sets a new standard in environmentally responsible architecture.

Architect: Behnisch, Behnisch & Partner, Workspace
Design: DEGW, 2004. Photo © Courtesy Genzyme Corporation

3 TRANSFORMING COMMUNITIES

Reconfiguration of social and economic activities, due to emerging location freedoms, will result in a new distribution of familiar building types and urban patterns.

INFORMATION TECHNOLOGIES can help re-energize public spaces, making them more responsive and humane.

José-Carlos Arnal

TECHNICAL ADVISOR TO THE MAYOR, CITY OF ZARAGOZA, SPAIN

Juan-Alberto Belloch

MAYOR OF ZARAGOZA, CITY OF ZARAGOZA, SPAIN

Dennis Frenchman

PROFESSOR OF THE PRACTICE OF URBAN DESIGN,
MASSACHUSETTS INSTITUTE OF TECHNOLOGY, UNITED STATES

Milla Digital Zaragoza: a new-century public realm

THE MILLA DIGITAL (DIGITAL MILE), a mile-long territory of technology-driven parks, public facilities and development, is now being created in the ancient city of Zaragoza, Spain. Designed with the assistance of the Massachusetts Institute of Technology (MIT) in the United States, the project will integrate digital media into the workings of everyday life, creating possibilities for new kinds of activities and physical places—and a new identity for the city.

City, innovation and jobs

TODAY, EVERY CITY WANTS TO BE A "CITY OF KNOWLEDGE," a new hot spot in the information-age landscape. There are sound economic reasons for those ambitions. Less than 10 per cent of total employment in the United States[1] is in manufacturing and there is increasing evidence that new, skilled jobs will come mainly from advanced service activities in the fields of information technology, content development, research, media, teaching, entertainment and creative services.[2] This is why urban planners are showing a growing interest in designing cities with attractive environments to draw new economic ventures and people.

Can urban design encourage the growth of true "innovation ecosystems" in existing cities? Some planners, academics, politicians and business developers think so. At the New Century Cities

---

1. "The Great Jobs Switch and Industrial Metamorphosis," *The Economist*, September 29, 2005.

2. Employment forecasts are always risky, but the evolution of post-industrial economies in the last decades suggests our assumption is right: Manuel Castells in *The Information Age: Economy, Society and Culture* (1996) confirms the increase of the "informational jobs" as a part of the total employment in the Group of Seven (G7) countries since 1970. Richard Florida in *The Rise of the Creative Class* (2002) sees a huge increase of the "creative jobs" until they account for 30 per cent of the total workforce.

137

Symposium,[3] held at MIT in January 2005, experts observed that there is a new generation of urban projects in Asia, Europe and the United States sharing the objective of positioning cities as key players in the digital era. Intensive, thoughtful use of new-media technologies—rethinking the way traditional city elements are designed and built—is the basis on which these projects are being achieved.

According to an assessment by MIT,[4] these kinds of new-century cities have these five characteristics in common:

- They involve very large-scale, multipurpose developments

- They promote innovation to achieve significant social and economic value for their host cities and, in some cases, host countries

- Information and media technologies are woven into the design of the cities

- They are eminently "liveable"

- The public and private sectors are intertwined

You can find these kinds of projects in cities such as New York; Cambridge, Massachusetts; Helsinki; Copenhagen; Seoul; Singapore and Zaragoza.

One of the more important ideas to emerge from the symposium was that business interests in cities are deeply tied to the quality of their public spaces. Among the success factors most appreciated by business and high-tech communities is the potential for social networking in the areas where people work, since social networking is the basis of all innovation processes. Providing opportunities for social networking in the public space is something at which cities have excelled for centuries—and will need to continue offering if people are to have safe, stimulating and prosperous places in which to live.

During the Milla Digital planning process, a city representative questioned a Cisco executive about the main criteria the company used to decide where new facilities should be located. The answer:

---

3. The symposium was jointly sponsored by the MIT Center for Real Estate and the City Design and Development group.

4. Dennis Frenchman, Michael Joroff, et al, *New Century Cities: Real Estate Value in a Digital World* (MIT Conference Prospectus, January 18, 2005).

"We are taking work to our workers; we go where our customers and the talented people are." The talented people to which Cisco referred are the creative, innovative, highly skilled, entrepreneurial types; the kinds of people who love the exciting atmosphere found in lively cities.

Understanding this, the city of Zaragoza reasoned that paying attention to public spaces would be a key element in creating the kind of city that would succeed in the digital economy—and provide the Milla Digital with a unique character.

Zaragoza and the Milla Digital

Roman emperor Caesar Augustus founded Zaragoza, located in north-eastern Spain. It is a mid-sized city of almost 700,000 inhabitants and is the capital of the Aragon region. With a strong industrial base, a comfortable socioeconomic status and 2,000 years of history, Zaragoza is hardly the location one would expect to harbour "digital dreams." The city's low international profile and weak presence in the service, creative and high-tech sectors, however, have cast a shadow on the possibility of maintaining its current prosperity in the future.

Milla Digital is not only an opportunity for a new building development, but it also will improve citizens' skills in dealing with the digital environment of today's information society.

Mindful of this situation, in 2003 Mayor Juan-Alberto Belloch decided to develop the Milla Digital project. The idea was to transform land surrounding the city's railroad infrastructure into a new district devoted to urban innovation. The site became feasible with the construction of a new, high-speed rail station at the edge of the city, freeing the old station site and tracking right-of-way and surrounding lands for redevelopment. Connecting the new and old station sites, the Milla Digital was seen not only as an opportunity for new building development, but also as a project that could accelerate Zaragoza into the information society—improving citizens' skills in dealing with a digital environment and creating new, highly skilled jobs for graduates of the city's many universities.

The Milla Digital is the centrepiece of strategic development already planned for the city, including International Exposition Zaragoza 2008 (a celebration of the dynamic relationship between water and human societies) and the high-speed train, which places Zaragoza within commuting distance of Madrid and Barcelona. These developments, together with the city's existing assets, provide an extraordinary opportunity to create a new global identity for Zaragoza, attracting new businesses and dramatically improving the infrastructure needed to maintain a high standard of living for its residents.

Work on the Milla Digital started in late 2006. The project comprises 1.07 million square metres of land, 4,000 new apartments, 243,000 square metres of office and commercial space and 231,000 square metres of public facilities, as well as a number of major green spaces and parks. These elements will be interconnected by a vast telecommunications network that is both wired and wireless. For example, fibre-optic cable will link all housing units, providing a massive test platform for new digital home products and services. In addition, the city has sought to integrate the Milla Digital with the historical and traditional fabric of the city, which is raising questions such as "How can IT be used to improve the design and performance of public spaces?" and "How can this new development contribute to the global identity of Zaragoza?"

The creation of an appropriate digital framework for the city's public spaces is as relevant and challenging as creating a physical structure.

To answer these questions, in 2005 the city signed a research agreement with MIT's Joint Program in City Design and Development, and the Media Lab, with the aim of creating a challenging vision for the Milla Digital. With the creation of an advisory committee by Mayor Belloch, which included several world-class sociologists, designers and IT experts,[5] the team focused on the potential of advanced communications and media technology in the development's public spaces. To date, the use of IT focuses mainly on the private sectors: home, new work environments and commercial entertainment. Integration of digital technology into the public space is the next milestone; this could reshape cities in the 21st century as the quality and

---

5. The list of members of this Zaragoza Advisory Committee is as follows: William J. Mitchell (chairman), François Bar, Manuel Castells, Dennis Frenchman, Peter Hall, Pekka Himanen, Michael Joroff, Véronique Kleck, Angela López, Guido Martinotti and Saskia Sassen.

performance of public spaces are the real core business of a city. Furthermore, the increasing importance of mobility to workplaces is creating an exciting opportunity to design public spaces that allow people to work on every corner, in every park or in every square.

Old city, new worlds

The research team realised early on that the Milla Digital, if successful, would add a new layer of culture to the city and would have to be carefully integrated with the previous, historic layers created by the Romans, Moors, Christians and the Industrial Revolution. The team proposed to use traditional elements of the city's form in the design and programming of the project as a way of creating continuity with Zaragoza's own unique identity. The Milla Digital will use elements that local citizens will easily recognise, giving them both a sense of inclusiveness and the experience of entering a new digital realm. These elements are:

- **Towers**—providing a unique image and voice

- **Walls**—defining edges to the city, inside and out

- **Layers**—culture, information and landscape

- **Bridges**—linking places, ideas, knowledge sources and experiences; switching between different layers of information in the physical and virtual worlds

- **Water**—connecting to the natural environment, with the issue of sustainability and the identity of Zaragoza operating as a centre for dealing with issues of water

The Milla Digital uses and reinterprets an ancient code of form to guide the physical framework of the site. This process involves organising elements along a pathway and linear park, called the Paseo del Agua, because of its innovative use of water. Two new development nodes anchor the Paseo, incorporating major public spaces and towers: Portillo, the site of the old train station and Almozara, across from the new station. At Almozara, a spectacular new pedestrian bridge will connect the Digital Mile to the high-speed rail station and neighbourhoods to the south and west. The pedestrian bridge will become a symbolic gateway to Zaragoza, spanning the highway that leads into the city from Madrid. The Paseo del Agua continues northward to the Expo 2008 site, which is accessed by a second pedestrian bridge across the Ebro River. Combined, the pathway, bridges, towers and public places will knit together the Digital Mile and provide an armature for multiple uses.

The Mile will provide a physical piece of continuity—a linear park between the old and the new stations—as a recognisable urban platform where new kinds of digital experiences can be developed. This concept of designing the city as both *hardware* and *software* will allow the project to connect disparate elements visually and functionally through a network of community and educational facilities—public spaces that serve multiple users and digital features.

Digital framework

The creation of an appropriate digital framework of software systems and content for the city's public spaces is as relevant and challenging as creating a physical structure. The Milla Digital experience will be supported by a digital framework comprising three layers:

1. **Ambient technology**—all of the spaces, parks and buildings in the Milla Digital will include free, public wireless connectivity to the Internet, as well as access to responsive media elements on the Mile. Location-based services will provide tailored content through cell phones or personal digital assistants at key spots providing, for example, historical interpretation of the Aljaferia palace or directions to the train station.

2. **Systems**—digital systems will facilitate public use and understanding of the environment, and will be concentrated along the pedestrian armature of the Mile. Proposed systems include intelligent street and building lights that can be accessed and programmed to change colour or intensity in response to the time of day, demands for use or artistic desires. Digital street furniture—café tables, bus stops, signage—will, for example, display information about the location of a bus stop or available parking spaces.

3. **Digital places**—principal nodes on the Digital Mile will include responsive elements that support different activities. Elements proposed for these places include digital facades (moveable components that can provide shade or modify spaces along the edges of buildings), paving that reflects patterns of use, "urban pixel" lighting that delineates the edges of space and "water walls" that respond to ambient conditions and human interaction.

The water wall is one example of how digital technology will affect qualities of place along the Mile. Developed for the Milla Digital by the MIT Media Lab, the water wall will be, on one hand, a fountain typical of the many already existing in Zaragoza, adding appeal to parks and squares. On other hand, the water wall will be a digital display—a curtain of water that can change flow patterns in response to people or the weather. So, the water may part as a child jumps through, or shut off if the wind blows, or be programmed to form images. Urban-scaled, the water wall can roll out along the entire Mile or be active in just some places, altering the geometry of those places to accommodate specific needs.

To make these functions possible, a dense network of telecommunications has been designed. Telecom carriers will benefit from generous infrastructure that will enable easier, less-expensive installation of wires and devices needed to provide sophisticated broadband services for commercial users. The Milla Digital will also have a large-capacity public telecom network devoted to providing connectivity to all of the intelligent furniture in the streets along with other digital features such as information systems, wireless displays and cultural facilities. This will make possible the evolution of a truly intelligent environment that serves as an urban-scaled test platform for creative ideas.

Campus Milla Digital

The framework for the Milla Digital will provide an exciting space for many different activities and experiments. But it also raises some challenging questions: Who will programme the digital activities and content on the Milla Digital and how will the spaces be activated? What are the technical and social standards that will allow easy access to digital elements and transfer of content without losing the originator's intentions, while at the same time ensuring that it is appropriate for public display?

Given that the Milla Digital is a large and dense central area of the city, the research team felt it would be a mistake to design and programme digital content in a centralised, top-down manner. Neither the city government nor the media companies are equipped for this role, and a new interface will be needed to connect the Milla Digital's capabilities with the needs and imagination of its users. To meet this challenge, two strategic actions need to be taken: establishing a new cultural management entity for the area known as the Campus Milla

143

Digital, and adopting an "open source" approach to the operation and programming of the public realm.

Campus Milla Digital will be a new kind of institution that will act as an intermediary between the infrastructure of the Milla Digital and its users. The campus will comprise two branches, which will act as bookends to the physical extent of the Milla Digital at Portillo and Almozara. At Portillo, the campus will include Museo de la Milla, aimed at engaging people of all ages with the digital side of city life and facilitating their knowledge, skills and access to digital resources and networks. At Almozara, the campus will focus on a new Centre for Arts and Technologies that is devoted to research, specialised training and exhibitions in the field of creative media. Each of these branches will be housed in an individual building that is part of a larger node of development. The two branches will function as a unit by providing complementary services and functions. Together, they will amalgamate a set of programmes that address a variety of audiences and needs, including cultural programming, content management, education and community outreach.

Functioning as a cultural and management institution, Campus Milla Digital will administer and provide access to existing and new information. It will link to existing resources in the city, such as municipal data, and facilitate access to services, education and training, ensuring the Milla Digital's sustainability over time. The campus will build new cultural and participatory programmes to enable the active and widespread use of the facilities on the Milla Digital. And, above all, it will strive to maintain the Milla Digital as an inclusive space where continuous experimentation and innovation can take place.

Open-source model

Open source is a simple programming concept: users are allowed to read, redistribute and modify the source code for a piece of software. Through their improvements and adjustments, the software evolves. Because the software is equally available to everyone, this evolutionary process can happen at an astonishing speed and produce a better product than the traditional, hierarchical programming model.[6]

---

6. Dennis Frenchman and Francisca Rojas, "Zaragoza's Digital Mile: Place-making in a New Public Realm," *Places*, Vol. 18, No. 3, third quarter, 2006.

Part of the appeal of public spaces is that they are already, to some degree, an open source. The public is able to co-opt areas of parks, squares and plazas for their own uses—eating lunch, reading the newspaper or playing sports. Advancing wireless technologies have allowed those uses to expand. In addition to recreational activities, public spaces now include education and work.

What will distinguish the Milla Digital is its integration of a built technological framework that both complements and improves upon existing modes of programming public space. Members of the public will be able to programme spaces along the Milla Digital not only by modifying their own activities, but also by changing the physical and sensual qualities of the spaces through digital intervention.

What will distinguish Milla Digital is its integration of a built technological framework that both complements and improves upon existing modes of programming public space.

Users may programme installations either through physical input by direct movement of their bodies in the space, which is then translated into digital signals, or through direct digital input entered through either stationary or mobile interfaces. Physical programming, both by proactive and incidental means, will create a lively environment that encourages physical movement and social activity. Meanwhile, the capacity for direct digital programming in a public arena will cultivate a culture of familiarity and comfort with the tools for controlling digital technology.

Direct digital programming could occur along a spectrum of skill levels: through touch screens, software or actual code writing. Regardless of the type of programming, output could be either physical or digital. And, the intervention may be local or remote: the programme could be at the other end of the Milla Digital or on the other side of the world.

An open-source approach to the local development of content and use of digital media along the Mile serves several purposes. First, it can help break down people's fear of technology by being a means of technological capacity building. Second, it can create a sense of ownership of the Mile for Zaragoza's residents. Third, it can provide a means through which a broader cross-section of people can construct and reveal their own narratives about the city's culture, functions and history. Of course, since the Mile will be a networked environment, remote development of content is also possible. That is to say, people could conceivably access, experience and contribute to the development of Zaragoza's Digital Mile from anywhere. This means that content can be produced at a global level and expressed in the physical environment at a local level, making the Digital Mile a place that defies geographical and political boundaries.

Members of the public will be able to programme spaces along the Milla Digital not only by modifying their own activities, but also by changing the physical and sensual qualities of the spaces through digital intervention.

Managing and programming digital public space through an open-source method does not imply a free-for-all. On the contrary, for an open-source community to be effective and sustainable, public contributions must be managed by a "producer" to ensure that they adhere to agreed-upon rules. These rules may govern certain issues such as equity of access, quality of content, timing or whatever else the community deems appropriate. For instance, changes to content may occur periodically—every day, every week or every minute. License to make changes may be limited to certain users who have been accredited. Alternately, the potential for change may be limited in scope but be completely nondiscriminating.

Conclusion

In a recent article, Professor Guido Martinotti argued that digital systems evolving over the past 20 years imply a new urban transition, equal in importance to earlier transitions made by cities, moving first to industry and then to a service economy.[7] As expressed by Martinotti, the Milla Digital is a project focused on the challenge of this digital transition, "trying to commit the cutting edges of the digital technology, not only to offer pleasant public spaces to the city, but also to recover the historical memory of the Aragonite city... and looking for this community in a new identity and a new role in the digital economy."

7. Guido Martinotti, "Saragozza alla sfida digitale," Il Sole 24 Ore, July 9, 2006.

The process is a creative act fuelled by the city's commitment to this ambitious initiative. Those involved know that much work remains to be done before the opportunities promised by digital media can be realised in the public realm. Many of those opportunities still need to be tested to see if they are really useful and valuable. Nevertheless, based on the work in Zaragoza, there are good reasons to believe that information technologies can help re-energise public spaces, making them more responsive and humane and reinforcing the key role that they have always played in the fabric and culture of the best cities.

JOSÉ-CARLOS ARNAL

TECHNICAL ADVISOR TO THE MAYOR, CITY OF ZARAGOZA, SPAIN

José-Carlos Arnal has a degree in media studies from the Autonomous University of Barcelona and a long professional career as a business journalist for regional media in Aragon. He is author of two books: *Sueños electrónicos* and *Creación de empresas: los mejores textos*, which cover the subjects of entrepreneurship and new economy ventures.

JUAN-ALBERTO BELLOCH

MAYOR, CITY OF ZARAGOZA, SPAIN

Juan-Alberto Belloch has a long and illustrious history of promoting democracy and human rights in Spain. He founded Judges for Democracy and the Association for Human Rights in the Basque Country.

As a judge, he has held various postings in La Gomera, Berga, Vic, and Alcoy, and was President of the Provincial Court in Vizcaya.

Belloch was Minister of Justice in Spain from 1993 to 1994 and Justice and Home Office minister from 1994-1996, in President Felipe Gonzalez's government. He was a member of the Spanish Parliament from 1996 to 2000 and senator for Zaragoza from 2000 to 2004. He became mayor of Zaragoza in June 2003 and is vice president of Expoagua Zaragoza 2008.

DENNIS FRENCHMAN

PROFESSOR OF THE PRACTICE OF URBAN DESIGN, MASSACHUSETTS INSTITUTE OF TECHNOLOGY (MIT) AND VICE PRESIDENT, ICON ARCHITECTURE, INC., UNITED STATES

Dennis Frenchman is professor of the Practice of Urban Design at MIT, where he is director of the City Design and Development group and chairs the Masters in City Planning program. He is also on the faculty of the Center for Real Estate, and is founding principal of ICON Architecture in Boston, an international architecture, urban design and planning firm.

Frenchman's practice and research focuses on the transformation of cities. He is an expert on the application of media technology to city design and has designed large-scale technology-driven developments, including Seoul Digital Media City, in Korea; International Media Avenue in Beijing, China; Sapiens in Florianopolis, Brazil; and the Digital Mile in Zaragoza, Spain. He is also principal investigator for the Digital Mile project (with William J. Mitchell). He has a particular interest in the redevelopment of industrial sites and has prepared plans for the renewal of textile mill towns, canals, rail corridors, steels mills, coal and oil fields, shipyards and ports.

Frenchman holds a master of architecture degree in advanced studies and a master of city planning degree, both from MIT.

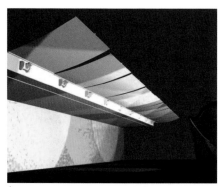

1

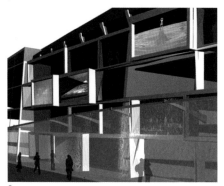

2

3

4

5

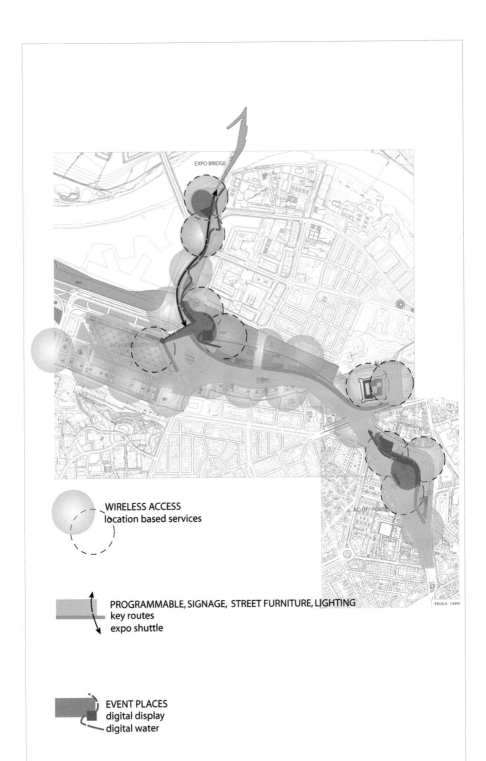

WIRELESS ACCESS
location based services

PROGRAMMABLE, SIGNAGE, STREET FURNITURE, LIGHTING
key routes
expo shuttle

EVENT PLACES
digital display
digital water

1&2 **Digital Awnings**

Digital Awnings, like the ones shown here, consist of moveable screens, which provide shade to the buildings. In addition, the awnings are also programmable surfaces on which the public can display interactive images using digital systems that are concentrated along the pedestrian armature of the Digital Mile.

Source: Michal Stangel, Massachusetts Institute of Technology

3 **The School of Media Arts and Sciences**

The School of Media Arts and Sciences integrates digital media into its building facade design. The digitally controlled water wall flows along the front of the building.

Source: Albert Wei, Massachusetts Institute of Technology

4 **Digital Memory Pavement**

A pathway along the Digital Mile uses "memory pavement" (digital ground surfacing) to record footsteps of pedestrians, displaying how often pathways are used. This technology makes residents and visitors aware of the physical impact their daily movements leave on the city, and is an artistic means of creating awareness for the interactive possibilities of digital technologies.

Source: Rajesh Kottamasu, Massachusetts Institute of Technology

5 **Digitally Controlled Water Wall**

The Water Wall is an urban scaled, interactive fountain system that has multiple purposes. On one hand, it serves as a typical fountain. On the other hand, it serves as a digital display, a curtain of water that changes flow in response to weather or to people jumping through it, as shown here.

Source: Andres Sevtsuk, Massachusetts Institute of Technology

6 **The Digital Mile**
The sequence of digital places along the Digital Mile consists of different layers of connectivity and media systems overlaid onto the physical urban design framework.

Source: Dennis Frenchman, Massachusetts Institute of Technology

INFORMATION AND COMMUNICATIONS TECHNOLOGY can be a competitive differentiator for building owners and developers, which creates additional economic value.

Dr. Sing Tien Foo
ASSOCIATE PROFESSOR, DEPARTMENT OF REAL ESTATE,
NATIONAL UNIVERSITY OF SINGAPORE, SINGAPORE

Connected Singapore: evolving from landlord to Facilities Service Provider

THERE MAY BE GROWING AWARENESS IN THE REAL ESTATE SECTOR about the benefits Information and Communications Technology (ICT) can bring to office tenants—but what does it mean for developers and owners? If more companies allow their employees to work remotely, will that not reduce the overall amount of office space required in the market? Similarly, if developers invest in technologies to make flexible workplaces easier, will it backfire and encourage their tenants to rent less space? And, will there be less demand for premium office space in city centers and easily accessible business parks, given that companies will be able to communicate virtually and no longer need to be close to their customers physically?

IT HAS NOT ALWAYS BEEN EASY to reach conclusions to these kinds of questions because of the conflicting market forces that come into play in the real estate market. For example, if owners provide services that meet tenants' needs, logically this should increase tenant loyalty. At the same time, however, statistical evidence suggests that tenants are demanding shorter lease terms and more flexible lease structures.

At the National University of Singapore, we have carried out research into these kinds of issues. Despite the potentially negative impact for owners, we have identified a number of upsides for real estate organizations that embrace ICT—upsides that have been proven over the course of a decade. There is evidence that adoption of ICT allows organizations to charge a premium for rent, for example, and also improves tenant retention—particularly where businesses feel that they are part of an evolving network of like-minded organizations, rather than merely tenants in a physical structure.

Benefits of connected offices

- 60 percent of developers perceive strong competition from ICT and broadband-ready office buildings

- 67 percent will respond with a strategy to upgrade connectivity

- 71 percent of developers expect ICT and broadband to enhance marketability

- 43 percent believe that ICT and broadband attract new tenants

- Post-upgrading effects:
    Improved occupancy rate (58 percent)
    Increased rent (46 percent)
    Increased operational and maintenance cost (61 percent)

- Intangible benefits:
    Enhanced landlord/tenant relationships
    Lowered leasing risks
    Improved market branding, image, and prestige

- Network value creation is estimated at 4 percent of unit rental value

Figure 1 Networked offices can charge more for rent because they provide new user experiences and operational efficiencies. Source: Dr. Sing Tien Foo, National University of Singapore, 2005.

In addition, ICT provides significant new revenue opportunities for landlords who are willing to take a more proactive approach to meeting their tenants' needs. Our studies show that there is a tangible business benefit for developers/owners who adopt the role of facilities service providers, using ICT to help their tenants grow their businesses while also generating new revenue streams for themselves.

Suntec City, a multipurpose development in Singapore's Marina District, is a case in point. Billed as "Asia's Vertical Silicon Valley," Suntec City is located at the fringe of the central business district, yet has managed to attract a number of well-known high-tech and financial-services clients. Its owners have created a perception of real value in the ICT capabilities they provide for tenants, and this connectivity—combined with the profile of the companies it has attracted and its ability to create a vibrant business network—has become a competitive differentiator. The proof is in its tenants' retention track records—even where newer premises become available, many of Suntec's older tenants stay put because of the combined benefits the site offers (see Figure 1).

A connected island

The vision of an intelligent island was developed to transform the city-state Singapore from a former British colony into a global center for science and technology, a high value-added and competitive location for production, and also a critical node in the global networks of trade, tourism, communication, and information.[1] Today it is the second-most competitive nation globally after the Unites States. Together, construction and real estate have been recognized as one of the major economic sectors in which ICT could be exploited. Various government agencies in Singapore have been driving ICT adoption in the real estate and construction industry since the early 1990s. COnstruction and Real Estate NETwork (CORENET) is the flagship ICT project undertaken to improve turnaround time, productivity, and performance of the construction and real estate sectors by re-engineering business processes with state-of-the-art ICT. This enables construction and real estate stakeholders to connect, communicate, and exchange information seamlessly and efficiently.

There is evidence that adoption of ICT allows organizations to charge a premium for rent, and also improves tenant retention.

Three areas of ICT-induced revolution can be expected in real estate and construction processes if the CORENET system is successfully implemented and accepted by users. First, compression of time and process is one possible outcome that can be facilitated via the integrated platform of CORENET. Second, knowledge content would receive growing attention from prospective CORENET users. Third, reconfiguration of business concept and scope may take place, which could, as a result, lead to the emergence of a new business model and the creation of ample business opportunities for CORENET users who possess the first-mover advantage. The ultimate CORENET goal is to create the IT infrastructure that will allow total integration across the basic processes of a building lifecycle—develop, design, procure, build, and operate (see Figure 2).

1. The vision to turn Singapore into a connected island has been described in the Connected Singapore and earlier Infocomm 21 plans, spearheaded by the Infocomm Development Authority (IDA) of Singapore (http://www.ida.gov.sg).

COnstruction and Real Estate NETwork

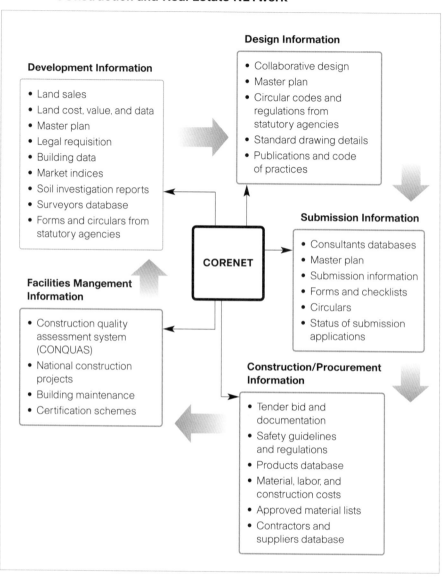

Development Information

- Land sales
- Land cost, value, and data
- Master plan
- Legal requisition
- Building data
- Market indices
- Soil investigation reports
- Surveyors database
- Forms and circulars from statutory agencies

Design Information

- Collaborative design
- Master plan
- Circular codes and regulations from statutory agencies
- Standard drawing details
- Publications and code of practices

CORENET

Submission Information

- Consultants databases
- Master plan
- Submission information
- Forms and checklists
- Circulars
- Status of submission applications

Facilities Mangement Information

- Construction quality assessment system (CONQUAS)
- National construction projects
- Building maintenance
- Certification schemes

Construction/Procurement Information

- Tender bid and documentation
- Safety guidelines and regulations
- Products database
- Material, labor, and construction costs
- Approved material lists
- Contractors and suppliers database

Figure 2 The COnstruction and Real Estate NETwork (CORENET) improves the productivity and performance of the real estate and construction industry by integrating business processes along the building lifecycle. Source: Building and Construction Authority, Singapore, 2006.

Changing user requirements

There has long been controversy over just how much impact ICT has actually made on demand for office space. Some have argued that, from a productivity perspective, ICT should drive a reduction in rental expenses—after all, if an organization becomes more productive, then, theoretically, it needs fewer people and, therefore, less space. But studies in the United States[2] and the United Kingdom[3] have demonstrated that the impact of this trend is far lower than might be expected. Likewise, there has been some concern about the impact that remote working will have on demand for office space. In an expanding economy, however, rent stabilizes, and the evidence so far is that the impact of remote working has not been significant.

In a survey of companies in the central business district of Singapore, we asked whether ICT leads to a reduction in office-space demand, and 50 percent of respondents who said "no" cited the belief that real estate decisions are taken independently of ICT.[4] It remains to be seen, then, how ICT improvements will directly reduce office-space demand.

We are experiencing a growing trend toward outsourcing of activities that are seen as peripheral.

Other ICT-related factors, however, are beginning to have a bigger impact. Real estate rents have traditionally been influenced by one overarching factor—location, location, location. In large part, this has been driven by what we call the "agglomeration effect," where people want to be centrally located and close to their customers. But increased connectivity reduces the requirement for spatially fixed office activities and, because of this, tenants are becoming more flexible about where they want to be located. ICT reduces the appeal and significance of a central business-district location. In some densely populated cities, such

2. W. C. Wheaton, "Telecommunications Technology and Real Estate: Some Perspective," working paper #63, Massachusetts Institute of Technology Center for Real Estate, Cambridge, Massachusetts, 1996.

3. V. A. Gibson and C. M. Lizieri, "Friction and Inertia: Business Change, Corporate Real Estate Portfolios and the U.K. Office Market," *Journal of Real Estate Research*, Vol. 22, No. 1/2, pp 59–79, 2001.

4. For details of the survey, refer to T. F. Sing, "Impact of Information and Communications Technology (ICT) on Real Estate Space: Perspective of Office Occupiers," Special issue on Technology and Real Estate, *Journal of Property Investment and Finance*, Vol. 23, No. 6, pp 494–505, 2005.

Physical office space matters

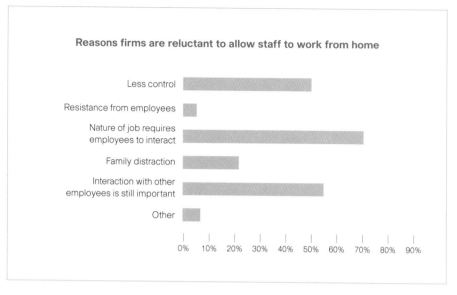

Reasons firms are reluctant to allow staff to work from home

Figure 3 Face-to-face interactions are the major reason firms are reluctant to allow employees to work remotely. Source: Dr. Sing Tien Foo, National University of Singapore, 2005.

as Singapore, which has roughly 6,000 persons per square kilometer, there is evidence that decentralization is starting to take place.

Similarly, we are experiencing a growing trend toward outsourcing of activities that are seen as peripheral. This applies to ICT itself, where owners are keen to offer technology services but do not want responsibility for maintaining the technical capability. But it also applies more broadly since improved connectivity allows organizations to outsource entire business functions, such as shifting a call center to India, which, in turn, frees up office space.

In addition, there is widespread evidence of tenants requiring greater flexibility, both in terms of the spaces they rent and the leases they sign. In the United Kingdom and other European countries, for example, tenants historically signed lengthy leases—sometimes as long as 20-plus years—because of the security it gave both parties. Increasingly, however, tenants are looking for shorter leases with more flexible terms. They also want greater flexibility in what they can do with the space they occupy. Going forward, we anticipate that three core factors will drive office-space changes: technology, demography, and changing business culture—all of which allow for new work practices.

Connected offices command premiums

These general trends have been borne out of our research at the National University of Singapore and the ICT-induced evolution of Singapore's office buildings. First, we have established that ICT-ready office buildings command a premium over other types of office space. Simply by bringing in greater broadband connectivity, organizations are able to increase rents. Second, the other side of this equation is that owners are concluding that without greater connectivity, tenant retention will suffer. We see more and more new buildings incorporating broadband into their designs, increasing the pressure on owners of premises without this capability to provide connectivity. This pressure has caused many developers/owners to spend millions of dollars on retrofits—raising floor levels and carrying out other major infrastructure work—to provide broadband connections (see Figure 1).

Ultimately, this will pave the way for the introduction of new workplace practices, such as flexible workspaces and remote working—although these are currently being approached with some caution. We recently carried out a survey among 432 businesses in the central business district of Singapore and found that 37 percent of respondents believe ICT will reduce the need for face-to-face meetings with clients. Approximately two-thirds of the respondents, however, will not let staff work from home. When we asked why, we found that 71 percent believe that the nature of their jobs requires employees to interact with staff and clients, while 57 percent feel that interaction with employees is still important. Half of those surveyed also felt they would lose control if staff worked from home (see Figure 3).

Increased connectivity reduces the need for spatially fixed office activities. Tenants are becoming more flexible about where they want to be located.

Workplace practice is largely a cultural issue, and approaches vary among different kinds of companies. For example, companies in IT, media, and advertising are more open to ideas such as flexible workplaces, while others, such as insurance and legal organizations, are less prepared to do so. This issue may also be related to company size. Many of the companies we interviewed occupy a relatively small space—2,500 square feet or less—and we found that 77 percent of them allocated less that 10 percent of their operating expense to ICT, which went to the purchase of the most commonly used desktop applications such as e-mail; more advanced technologies, such as videoconferencing, are yet to be widely adopted.

Suntec City—a Facilities Service Provider

Suntec City is the largest commercial real estate development in Singapore. It was developed by a group of 11 Hong Kong tycoons on a 117,000-square-meter commercial site sold by the Urban Redevelopment Authority (URA) of Singapore in December 1988. The land was developed into a fully integrated project with a convention and exhibition center, five office towers, and a shopping and entertainment center. Envisioned as a "city within a city," the US$2.3 billion Suntec City project offers 4.3 million square feet of office, retail, and conference facilities. The development has effectively embraced broadband connectivity and ICT to position the project as one of the most sought-after commercial spaces in Singapore (see Figure 4).

Figure 4 Suntec City. Suntec City is an example of how physical connectivity and digital technology improve real estate values. Businesses are part of an evolving network of like-minded organizations rather than merely tenants in a physical structure.
Masterplan Architect: I. M. Pei and Partners, 1989. Source: The management of Suntec City.

We carried out a study with Mr. Wong Ah Long, the former CEO of Suntec City. Our findings showed that Suntec City was built on reclaimed land, and does not have the location advantages of the central business district. What it does have, however, is a different approach.

First, the landlord positions itself as a Facilities Service Provider (FSP).[5] While a typical operator is primarily interested in collecting rent, an FSP takes a more proactive approach, paying closer attention to tenants' needs. The aim is to enhance the building's offering to attract tenants in the first instance, and then retain them by providing an environment that helps each tenant grow its business. This opens up a host of new revenue streams for the provider, and tenants are increasingly willing to pay a premium for ICT services. In a simulation exercise, using reasonable assumptions of the input variables, a differentiating premium of close to 4 percent was estimated as the economic value for ICT connectivity in a hypothetical building.[6]

The development has effectively embraced broadband connectivity and ICT to position the project as one of the most sought-after commercial spaces in Singapore.

Second, from the beginning, Suntec had a goal of making the buildings connected and ICT-friendly. A slew of ICT and broadband initiatives—which include fiber-optic broadband access, instant networking, digital offices, a common telecommunication connection, an Internet call center, a plug-and-play environment, fourth-generation wireless communications networks, wireless broadband services, and many others—have been implemented in phases in the so-called "Suntec IT Waves" projects. Wong Ah Long believed in "perceived value"—in other words, in creating a public perception and positive brand image that leads people to place higher value on the development than on the average market value. The Waves project complemented this image by creating a business network within the development, bringing

---

5. This FSP business concept has been successfully patented by Suntec City in Hong Kong and Taiwan. The patent (#10/010/319), titled "System and Method for Increasing Perceived Value of a Property to Tenants," has also been filed in the United States.

6. T .F. Sing, K. P. J. Lee, and A. L. Wong, "Network Effects and Broadband Connectivity in Office Building," *International Real Estate Review*, Vol. 5, No. 1, pp 146–168, 2002.

in complementary companies and organizing activities to bring businesses and individual tenants together. A substantial proportion of tenants are information-technology companies or finance companies, including Microsoft and Fujitsu.

It is clear that this approach works. Suntec survived the financial crisis of 1997 and 1998 when office buildings in the central business district suffered a drop in rentals: its own decrease was smaller than average, and some units were able to sustain their rental value. Based on a sub-sample of 234 new office leases in Suntec from 1997 to 1999, the average unit gross rents declined by 11.32 percent and 4.1 percent in 1998 and 1999, respectively, whereas the average rents for the Central Area as reported by the URA Rental Index declined by larger margins of 16.39 percent and 9.5 percent, respectively, over the same two-year period.

We asked the tenants at Suntec what attracted them to the development. Some responses focused on traditional attributes: prestigious office buildings, competitive rent, and conventional amenities, such as hotels and shopping centers. But there were also a number of differentiating factors; tenants referred to the pro-business environment, the lease structure, the quality of the workplace, accessibility, broadband communications, and international connectivity. Each of these factors can be attributed to Suntec's FSP philosophy.

Connectivity enables a business network across the development to bring complementary businesses and individual tenants together.

We also established from some tenants that the ICT infrastructure was a clear driver in their decision to move to Suntec City. In some cases, this came down to business pragmatism—an organization might want to be located close to a key business partner, such as Microsoft, for example. In other cases, however, their decision had more to do with agglomeration, particularly among longer-standing tenants that had built up a network within the development. The combination of the ICT-friendly business infrastructure and the network effect was enough to keep them in the building, despite the fact that new offices had subsequently been built nearby, offering more modern buildings.[7]

7. T. F. Sing, T. L. J. Ooi; A. L. Wong, and K. K. P. Lum, "Network Connectivity and Office Occupiers' Space Decision—The Case of Suntec City," *Journal of Property Investment & Finance*, Vol. 24, No. 4, 2006.

We believe that proactive tenant management is key to attracting and retaining high-value tenants, and presents significant new opportunities for owners.

The positive response from tenants means Suntec has an advantage that grows over time. Other buildings can offer ICT—but Suntec has developed a social and digital network that cannot be replicated overnight. We expect that the lessons being learned in Singapore will be replicated elsewhere around the world. It is clear from our research that ICT can be a competitive differentiator for owners/developers, which can create additional economic benefits. More fundamentally, however, ICT is an enabler of the Facilities Service Provider concept, which will take real estate management to a new dimension. We believe that proactive tenant management—using business networks and technologies to create a beneficial working environment—is key to attracting and retaining high-value tenants, and presents significant new opportunities for owners.

DR. SING TIEN FOO

ASSOCIATE PROFESSOR, DEPARTMENT OF REAL ESTATE,
NATIONAL UNIVERSITY OF SINGAPORE, SINGAPORE

Dr. Sing Tien Foo completed his doctorate at the University of Cambridge, in the United Kingdom, in 1999 under the Cambridge Commonwealth Trust scholarship and the Overseas Research Students award. He also holds a master of philosophy degree in land economy from the University of Cambridge and a bachelor of science degree, with first-class honors, in estate management from the National University of Singapore.

He is undertaking research on issues relating to connectivity in real estate space and its impact on real estate space demand. His other research interests include real options theory, credit risk analyses, and securitization.

Dr. Tien Foo has been a director of the Asian Real Estate Society Board since 2000. He serves as an editorial board member for the *International Real Estate Review* journal and *Pacific Rim Property Research Journal.*

DIGITAL BEIJING will show both historical retrospectives and forward-looking innovations that demonstrate how technology influences work styles and lifestyles in China and abroad.

Zhu Yan
DIRECTOR GENERAL, BEIJING MUNICIPAL OFFICE OF INFORMATIZATION, CHINA

Building Digital Beijing

One of the world's oldest capital cities, 3,000-year-old Beijing is racing into the 21st century. For the first time, China is hosting an Olympic Games in 2008, and the honor is a source of enormous national pride. The Beijing Organizing Committee for the XXIX Olympiad (www.beijing-2008.org) has dubbed this event the Digital Olympics, reflecting China's desire to incorporate advanced technologies throughout the Games. The committee seeks to deliver communications services that enable anyone—anyplace, anytime—to enhance their enjoyment of the Games through secure, high-speed communications services that are convenient and efficient.

Preparation for the Games is accelerating an ambitious city plan called Digital Beijing, which is launching the ancient city into the digital age with a fully integrated, high-speed digital communications infrastructure supporting cutting-edge information services, such as digital television, wireless Internet access to government, e-commerce Websites, and mobile telephony. With individualized, multilingual support, these services will cater to the many needs of international participants, visitors, and local citizens during the Games and for many years afterward.

The cornerstone of Digital Beijing is the Digital Beijing Building, a dramatic edifice that represents the impact of digital technology in our 21st-century world (see photograph 1). With a profile resembling a giant bar code and light-emitting diode facades suggesting the complex, integrated circuitry of silicon chips, this unique building will act as the nerve center for the Games, enabling communications among support staff, security personnel, international journalists, and television crews in the many Games venues throughout Beijing and five outlying cities.

The Digital Beijing Building will perform an essential role in China's vision of bringing technology out of the labs and into the lives of its citizens. As one element of China's national digital communications and e-government services strategy, the 96,000-square-meter facility is a focal point for public and corporate explorations into the digital era. The building will serve as a command center for major communications development and activities in Beijing and throughout China. It is designed to accommodate continual enhancements to maintain its status as a showcase for the latest advances in digital technology. It will house both government employees and private organizations, and operate in a manner that inspires Chinese government agencies and businesses to use technology to change working practices and become more efficient.

Digital Beijing is launching the ancient city into the digital age with a fully integrated, high-speed digital communications infrastructure supporting cutting-edge information services.

After the Games, the Digital Beijing Museum will educate visitors about the achievements and potential of innovative technologies. As part of the Digital Beijing Building, the museum will show both historical retrospectives and forward-looking innovations that demonstrate how technology influences work styles and lifestyles in China and abroad. Exhibits and displays will encourage visitors to interact with IT devices to learn about technology (see photograph 1). Initial exhibits may feature wireless access to the Internet or government Websites. One idea in development is a giant personal computer model that people can tour, touching and interacting with the technology in a new, engaging manner.

China's vision of bringing technology out of the labs and into the lives of its citizens will be realized with the Digital Beijing Building.

Visitors will view a real data center through glass walls, learning what each component does and how it works. They will also see examples of technology in government and industry that invite them to speculate about future enhancements and changes. Frequently changing exhibits will attract visitors to return again and again to learn more.

The ambitious scope and public showcase quality of the Digital Beijing Building requires a coordinated effort among many agencies and planning teams to succeed. Through this effort, the committee hopes to exceed international expectations for a high-technology Games with a uniquely Chinese character. The world eagerly awaits the debut of the Digital Beijing Building in 2007. China anticipates that the project is the beginning of a dynamic, innovative legacy that gives it a leadership role in the worldwide digital era.

ZHU YAN

DIRECTOR GENERAL, BEIJING MUNICIPAL OFFICE OF INFORMATIZATION, CHINA

Zhu Yan is the Director General of the Beijing Municipal Office of Informatization with responsibility for leading the construction of Digital Beijing and the 2008 Digital Olympics.

Previously, he was the executive director of the Beijing Municipal Commission of Science and Technology, and has over 10 years' experience in high-tech administration.

Born in Beijing in 1963, he has a master's degree in business administration from Tsinghua University in China.

Digital Images

1 **The Digital Beijing Building**
The Digital Beijing Building is the cornerstone of the 2008 Olympic Games, and represents the impact of digital technology on our 21st-century world. With a profile resembling a giant bar code and facades lighted by light-emitting diodes, the building will be the central point for the Games. The Digital Beijing Building houses government employees and private organizations and is designed to educate visitors about technology achievements and innovations. Digital exhibits and displays are integrated into the physical fabric of the building, encouraging visitors to interact with technology.

Architect: Studio Pei-Zhu, 2005

THE VISION of information technology-integrated buildings that produce more energy onsite than is brought to them in the form of non-renewable resources is today realizable.

Dr. Volker Hartkopf
DIRECTOR, CENTER FOR BUILDING PERFORMANCE AND DIAGNOSTICS,
CARNEGIE MELLON UNIVERSITY, UNITED STATES

Vivian Loftness
UNIVERSITY PROFESSOR OF ARCHITECTURE,
CARNEGIE MELLON UNIVERSITY, UNITED STATES

Strategies for sustainable built environments

BUILT ENVIRONMENTS AFFECT OUR DAILY LIVES on global, national, corporate, and personal levels. We face limits and dangers, however, resulting from energy consumption, carbon dioxide gas emissions, and chemical toxicity. Our current methods for designing, building, and operating these environments are not sustainable.

HOW SHOULD OUR BUILT ENVIRONMENTS FUNCTION—will they provide the nourishment, comfort, health, community, and a shared quality of life, including mobility and livability? Or will our built environments become squalor amidst a collapsing climate?

We need to develop, demonstrate, and deploy sustainable built environment practices rapidly, on a worldwide basis. The built environment must be able to respond to the dynamics of weather and climate, and to maximize usage of natural resources in a restorative manner. We need to create built environments that improve what exists rather than just doing less harm.

No single discipline owns sustainability. Progressive environmental leadership must draw from ethics, economics, science, technology, and public policy. Progress depends on the successful integration of political, social, technical, and individual systems.

A looming crisis

The United States uses vast amounts of energy to drive industry and commerce, and to maintain its lifestyles. At present, the United States has 4 percent of the world's population and consumes 23.6 percent of the world's non-renewable energy resources. Further, the United States and the emerging economies of China and India emit an enormous amount of pollution as a side effect of energy consumption. Currently, projected carbon dioxide emissions from China, India, and the United States could rise to nearly seven times current annual rates by 2050 (Figure 1).

Projected carbon dioxide emissions

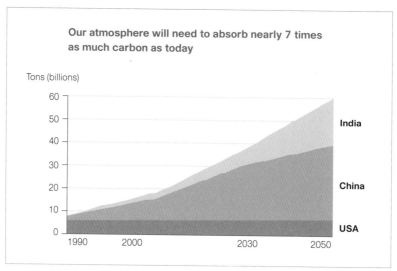

Figure 1 An alarming trend in carbon dioxide emissions looms from China and India. Source: Center for Building Performance and Diagnostics, NSF/IUCRC and ABSIC, Carnegie Mellon University, 2006.

About 70 percent[1] of all electricity in the United States—almost 40 percent of all primary energy—goes toward building operations. Including the manufacture and transport of building materials, components, and systems, this amount increases to more than 50 percent of primary—and almost 90 percent of electric—energy consumption.

Of the 70 percent of the United States' electricity consumed to condition buildings, more than 50 percent comes from coal, which contributes almost twice as much emissions as gas-fired power plants. This translates to about 4.5 trillion pounds of carbon dioxide each year. Therefore, the external environmental impact of building energy consumption is immense, degrading human respiratory well being, the viability of natural systems, and our economic performance.

Present design and engineering practices lead to static buildings and their conditioning by centralized and bulk solutions. Commercial buildings with climatically unresponsive, sealed facades and envelopes do not allow for natural ventilation, ignore the climate, or even fight it, and are predominantly not daylighted. They overheat in summer and often in spring and fall, leading to enormous cooling loads.

1. Energy Information Administration/Annual Energy Review 2001. Fig. 8.5.

172

Sustainable building concepts

In order to develop sustainable practices, the building envelopes—facade and roofs—have to become dynamic, akin to living membranes that harvest sun, water, and air, and re-create soil. Such a concept provides for day lighting, natural ventilation, and passive heating and cooling, as well as energy generation (solar thermal, photovoltaic, and wind). Initially, this can lead sustainability efforts and, in the medium-term, help eliminate usage of non-renewable resources for the operations of the built environment.

Fortunately, there is enormous potential for dramatic improvements in the performance of the built environment through the integration of systems. A major opportunity lies in an integrated view of the simultaneous improvements that can be achieved in health, well being, and productivity of occupants.

We present four major concepts and related opportunities to drive drastic improvements in energy and environmental effectiveness of commercial buildings, while simultaneously increasing occupant health and organizational effectiveness.

- Dynamic envelopes negotiate external weather and climatic conditions to the benefit of interior occupancy requirements, including thermal, visual, acoustic, and air quality, while conserving non-renewable resources.

- Buildings as theaters meet organizational requirements on demand. This uses an integrated platform for all services, offering flexibly through plug-and-play terminal units to provide access to ventilation, power, communication, controls, and data systems. This flexibility eliminates waste and simplifies the process of spatial reconfiguration.

- By integrating energy conservation with renewable energy and distributed energy technologies, buildings can become energy generators. Buildings function as power plants, producing more energy onsite than is brought to them in the form of non-renewable resources.

- Advanced, integrated sensing, actuating, and control technologies and their network-enabled interaction are critically required to enable successful operations of buildings with the integrated systems described above.

The dynamic envelope

Buildings need to be enclosed by living membranes, reacting to external climatic and weather conditions in order to create desired states. This means harvesting daylight, passive/active heating and cooling, natural ventilation, and rainwater. It would regenerate or restore landscapes.

To enable energy and environmentally efficient practices, mixed-mode conditioning systems are increasingly being embraced in Europe. Mixed-mode systems include operable windows and vents through facade ventilation, desiccant dehumidification, passive/active solar systems, flexible zones, and non-air-conditioned parts of buildings. Inhabitants favor buildings with these systems over the stifling, recirculated-air monoliths that assume uniformity in occupant needs. Consequently, living membranes, combined with multimodal building systems, increase human health and productivity while saving considerable amounts of energy. Mixed-mode systems can provide almost 100 percent return on investment.[2]

Mixed-mode systems are appropriate for both new and established structures, including low- and medium-rise buildings in temperate and cold climate zones. These buildings enjoy reduced heating, ventilation, and air conditioning (HVAC) costs.

Buildings as theaters

The building is a theater stage, providing plug-and-play access to building services such as water, air, electricity, and communication (data, voice, video, and controls). On top of the platform would be adjustable "stage sets," allowing on-demand changes in location and density of occupants and equipment. This system allows for changes in the amount of enclosure needed for individuals and teams of all sizes.

A new, flexible infrastructure that can change both location and density of occupants, equipment, and services, as well as the amount of enclosure around them, does allow spaces to be reconfigured easily, quickly, and cheaply without creating waste. This approach leads to more effective use of interior real estate by offering employees a choice of work places to meet their work styles and requirements. It accomplishes this by increasing workspace utilization, and by enabling occupants to create work environments that meet their requirements on demand.

---

2. See e-BID: http://cbpd.arc.cmu.edu/ebids/

Energy strategies

Building on the experiences with the Robert L. Preger Intelligent Workplace (IW) at Carnegie Mellon University (CMU), the "living" and "lived-in" laboratory at the Center for Building Performance and Diagnostics (CBPD), which researches the performance of innovative building products integrated into an actual working office, is now designing and engineering the Building as Power Plant/Invention Works (BAPP) project on campus. The IW has pioneered building innovations in the creation of settings for occupant comfort, health, and productivity; organizational effectiveness; technological adaptability; as well as energy and environmental effectiveness throughout the lifecycles of all materials, components, and systems. The Center is also developing advanced techniques and concepts in information technology.

This research will usher in building technologies and systems that generate more energy onsite than will be brought to buildings in the form of non-renewable resources. The basic principle is highest efficiency in energy conversion through combined heating, cooling, and power generation, augmented by advanced solar thermal-driven absorption chiller and heating and geothermal technologies. The BAPP addresses significant national and international needs in terms of energy effectiveness, energy quality, reliability, security, and environmental performances.

Ultimately, bio-fuels and other renewable resources will replace non-renewable resources, such as natural gas.

An "ascending-cascading energy scheme" integrates energy generation, building HVAC, and lighting technologies (Figure 2). The right side of the diagram depicts an "ascending strategy." The fenestration, shading, and building mass is configured to minimize the lighting, cooling, and heating loads, and to maximize the number of months for which neither artificial cooling nor heating is needed. Then passive strategies are introduced, such as cross-ventilation, stack ventilation, fan-assisted ventilation, and night ventilation. Passive cooling is followed by desiccant cooling when humidity levels exceed the comfort zone. Geothermal energy activates the building mass for cooling and heating. As outdoor temperatures or indoor heat loads

The building as a power plant

Figure 2 BAPP = Building as a Power Plant. The central concepts of the BAPP are cascading and ascending strategies of energy generation and utilization. Source: Carnegie Mellon University, 2006.

exceed the capability of these systems, the building uses solar thermal and/or reject heat from power generation by means of absorption cooling systems. Only as a last resort is a task-ambient, central-system refrigerant cooling system employed.

Complementing the "ascending" energy strategy is a "cascading" energy strategy, designed to maximize use of limited non-renewable resources. In building power generation, reject heat from the fuel cell, biodiesel engine generator, or gas turbine can be converted into steam, which drives a steam turbine. In the cascading system, reject heat drives desiccant, absorption refrigerant systems. Resulting reject heat can be used for space and domestic hot water heating. Ultimately, bio-fuels and other renewable resources will replace non-renewable resources, such as natural gas.

Sensors, controls, and IT

Future sensor and sensor network systems must successfully address the following factors:

- User needs and decision support to create comfortable, healthy, and productive settings

- Organizational requirements for flexibility

- Technological adaptability to ensure easy introduction of new technology, and the removal of outdated technology, without waste

- Energy and environmental effectiveness in operation and maintenance throughout the building's lifecycle

Integrated design stands on the pillars of human needs for healthful, safe, and productive environments; on societal needs for energy, resources, and security; and on environmental needs for healthy and diverse ecological systems. To develop a new model for integrated design, new metrics for accurately assessing the cost effectiveness of alternative design scenarios for enhanced health and productivity in high-performance buildings must be developed, including cost-effective monitoring tools and control strategies that can be integrated into the next generation of automated building control systems.

Therefore, Carnegie Mellon, in close cooperation with the industry, is developing ubiquitous, flexible, re-addressable, and wireless sensing systems, combined with advanced logic concepts. These systems have to be integrated with flexible, adaptable, and responsive building technologies, such as those that have been realized in the IW. These new sensing systems require advanced decision making processes that have distributed intelligence. The distributed intelligence aspect could then be a major gateway to advance the entire field of sensing systems.

A vision of the future

Imagine arriving at your workspace, which tells you all the devices available for control, all the sensors available for input, and all the levels of control choices at your command. Imagine an online meter that informs you of the energy and environmental performance of your space or building compared to others, international norms, and potentials given the capabilities of your devices (Figure 3).

This vision is now realizable with advances in IT infrastructures and software innovations. Every fixture in a workspace can be addressed: lights, air diffusers, radiators, blinds, window openers, PCs, printers, radios, and locks. The IW is pursuing this future vision as the Information Technology Enabled Sustainability Test bed (ITEST).

ITEST innovations are built around the existence of a common cabling and wiring infrastructure backbone. Each fixture identifies itself, and its Internet address reveals the level of control that is available to each occupant. ITEST provides a simple user interface for each fixture or collection of fixtures with access to the on-off, temperature, dimming, or time-of-day controls as needed, all graphically shown on a personal digital assistant (PDA), laptop, or desktop computer. In addition, an expanding range of sensors can also be plugged into the network backbone to monitor light levels, temperature, air quality conditions, occupancy presence, and more. Users can check existing

Information technology-enabled sustainability

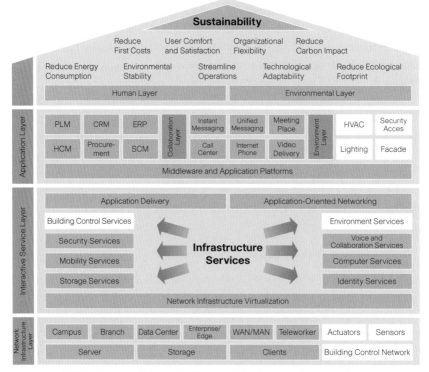

Figure 3 CRM = Customer Relationship Manager, ERP = Enterprise Resource Planning, HCM = Human Capital Management, HVAC = Heating, Lighting, Air Conditioning, PLM = Product Lifecycle Management, SCM = Supply Chain Management.

Critical to the success of Information Technology-Enabled Sustainability is the convergence of building systems and information technologies. This diagram illustrates the integration of building systems (white) in the intelligent information network architecture. The resulting networking benefits for humans and the environment are shown in the top triangle.
Source: Carnegie Mellon University, 2006.

conditions to improve performance or simply let sensors talk to controllers directly. Each measure taken on the sensor or the controller is actually an event, recorded on the End-to-End Diagnostic Discovery (EDDY) network, developed at CMU. This enables decision makers to collect meaningful data on every environmental condition, to control actions taken to improve overall energy performance, or to engage a central energy management system to pursue a strategy of peak-load shaving and energy conservation.

Imagine arriving at your workspace, which tells you all the devices available for control, all the sensors available for input, and all the levels of control choices at your command.

Power over Ethernet (PoE) eliminates duplicate wiring and helps pay for installation of addressable fixtures. Plugging an addressable fixture into a network helps users recognize the level of control they have, and finances additional controls as needed—environmentally enriching the building over time. Controls can be set to respond to timers. Creation of a communications backbone to support addressable environmental sensors and controllers allows users to know controllable environmental conditioning devices and which levels of control are available to balance sustainability and comfort.

ITEST is being designed to negotiate and meet building-control requirements based on the central repository of sensor data from local sensors and offsite sensors on the Web. Furthermore, it will also analyze historic records of sensor and controller readings to establish environmental costs over time and satisfy environmental conditions to support energy, security, comfort, and air quality optimization.

The consequences of connectivity

Crucial to the success of projects such as ITEST is the integration of technologies that previously operated in separate silos, such as ventilation air, thermal conditioning, power, data, voice, and video networks.

Connectivity has a central role in managing technologies to create energy effectiveness. It could:

- Enable the use of renewable forms of energy

- Operate advanced built environments while conserving non-renewable resources

- Enable distributed electric energy generation with rejected heat utilization

- Create buildings that meet high levels of occupant comfort

- Lead to occupant productivity and health

- Achieve organizational effectiveness

- Enable technological adaptability

- Achieve energy and environmental effectiveness throughout the lifecycles of all materials, components, and systems

Advanced and integrated sensing, actuating, and control systems can help realize levels of energy conservation previously unimaginable. The vision revolves around Internet-enabled communications, with almost every activity generating a data point. Every fixture in buildings can be addressable, resulting in long-term functional flexibility and technological adaptability.

It could go further and precondition the building in advance of changes, using the weather report, for instance. Different strategies would be needed depending on the types and speed of environmental change required. The weather can be predicted reliably some hours in advance. The building filling up with people unexpectedly cannot be planned for, and would result in increased heat, humidity, and carbon dioxide levels. Sensors in a Micro/Electro/Mechanical System (MEMS), being wireless, can be deployed wherever they are required. They can also watch over each other to produce a self-healing system, so if one sensor were to signal strange results, the others can take a majority decision as to whether that result makes sense in that particular context.

Connectivity has a central role in managing technologies to create energy effectiveness.

Plugging an addressable fixture into a network helps users recognize the level of control they have, and enables the purchase of additional controls as needed, environmentally enriching the building over time. Controls can be set to respond to timers, and sensors can be activated to turn on lights when it is dark, to accommodate personal preferences or to respond to environmentally strategic commands.

So, in combination with these dynamic building enclosure and interior systems, the technology operates the building energy systems efficiently and effectively, considering climate, weather, and occupancy patterns, as well as individual and group task requirements.

The vision to embed intelligence into the physical fabric of the building is today realizable. With control comes the ability to match the energy input to the requirements of both occupants and the environment.

To many, this vision may seem beyond the realistic reach of today's technology. But the technology is here now, and we can achieve everything discussed here. Ultimately, we have no alternative but to create more effective buildings, and to find different, new ways of generating the power we need for our comfort and survival. To continue with our present unsustainable methods is simply not a viable option.

DR. VOLKER HARTKOPF

DIRECTOR, CENTER FOR BUILDING PERFORMANCE AND DIAGNOSTICS,
CARNEGIE MELLON UNIVERSITY, UNITED STATES

Volker Hartkopf has been teaching and conducting research at Carnegie Mellon University since 1972. His work covers a broad range of activities: international initiatives, funded research and professional consulting on building systems integration, advanced technology, building performance, energy conservation, urban revitalization, third-world housing, and disaster prevention. As an architect, he has designed building projects in Germany, Bangladesh, Peru, and the United States. He also led master planning projects for Volkswagen A.G. and the city of Wolfsburg, Germany; EXPO 2000 Hanover; and Berlin-Lichtenberg, Germany.

In 1975, Hartkopf co-initiated and subsequently directed the first multi-disciplinary program in Architecture, Engineering, and Planning in the U.S. In 1981, he co-founded the Center for Building Performance and Diagnostics (CBPD) at Carnegie Mellon and between 1981 and 1985, developed jointly with Vivian Loftness and Peter A.D. Mill the Total Building Performance Evaluation Method at Public Works in Canada. Hartkopf created and directs the Advanced Building Systems Integration Consortium (ABSIC), which focuses on the impact of advanced technology on the physical, environmental, and social settings in office buildings, toward creating high performance work environments. Currently, Hartkopf is leading the Building as Power Plant (BAPP) project, selected by the U.S. Congress as the National Test-bed for Advanced Technology in Building.

VIVIAN LOFTNESS

UNIVERSITY PROFESSOR OF ARCHITECTURE,
CARNEGIE MELLON UNIVERSITY, UNITED STATES

Vivian Loftness is an internationally renowned researcher, author, and educator with over 30 years of focus on environmental design and sustainability, advanced building systems, and systems integration, climate, and regionalism in architecture, as well as design for performance in the workplace of the future. She is a key contributor to the development of the Intelligent Workplace at Carnegie Mellon University—a living laboratory of commercial building innovations for performance—and has authored a range of publications on international advances in the workplace.

She has served on six National Academy of Science panels, as well as being a member of the Academy's Board on Infrastructure and the Constructed Environment, and has given three Congressional testimonies on sustainable design.

From 1994-2004, she was Head of the School of Architecture at Carnegie Mellon University.

THE GOAL is not to build wired buildings and cities, but to create inspirational buildings and cities in which technology enables personal lifestyle choices and corporate innovation.

Stanley C. Gale
CHAIRMAN, GALE INTERNATIONAL, UNITED STATES

New Songdo City: building experiences, interactions, and a new way of living

REAL-ESTATE VISIONARIES DON'T BUILD BUILDINGS. We build experiences, interactions, and a way of living. That is, we build with an eye toward the *possibilities* inherent in a particular structure, in a particular place, at a particular time. It is a very hopeful profession in that sense.

IMAGINE, THEN, the breathtaking sense of possibility involved in the creation of an entirely new city. The challenge of New Songdo City, the metropolis Gale International is constructing near Incheon, South Korea, is to fashion a successful urban environment for the 21st century. The yardsticks are many: economic, social, environmental. Technology is the enabler for much of that value creation, but we contend that our vision of the city and the life it makes possible is the underpinning for those wires and networks, not the other way around.

Creating a "ubiquitous city," or "U-City," in which all major information systems (residential, medical, business, and so on) share data—computers are built into the houses, streets, and office buildings; and the technology and facilities infrastructures are integrated—would be a gargantuan challenge for an existing city. In the case of Songdo, it is the easy part. Since Songdo is a completely new city, it serves as a blank canvas on which to imagine and implement a technology vision without having to incorporate existing buildings or legacy networks. Songdo also has the advantage of being located in a nation that boasts an extraordinary level of technological acumen, the highest penetration and variety of broadband services, and a population that is probably the most computer literate—and demanding—on Earth.

The more difficult test is planning for the emergence of a "U-Culture" that is energizing and enabling, that results in applications both serendipitous and unpredictable, and where citizens will decide for themselves what kind of digital life they want. This challenge deeply informed the hypotheses behind the design of Songdo and its technology infrastructure, as well as the concept of Songdo as an experimental test bed for new digital applications on a scale—an entire city—unique in the world. Songdo's integrated facilities management service provider, Songdo U-Life, LLC, will partner with high-tech companies around the world that can similarly envision these possibilities.

All major city, building, and information technology infrastructures in a ubiquitous city are integrated and part of the urban design.

Broadband connectivity (wired and wireless) is now viewed as a *de rigueur* infrastructure element in everything from individual buildings to large-scale urban developments. As a result, developers and builders tend to see technology as an end in itself, a necessary amenity that in many ways is no different from any other amenities that can be marketed to buyers and tenants, whether they be granite kitchen counters or teak-paneled conference rooms. But a marble counter, while a status symbol, doesn't inspire a new way of cooking, and an impressive conference room doesn't prompt a new kind of business practice.

Technology is both an amenity and an enabler, and the best of our new residential and commercial buildings—and certainly the best of our urban designs—step back to look at how architecture and planning can encourage new, and perhaps unexpected, activities. The goal is not to build wired buildings and cities, but to create inspirational buildings and cities in which technology enables personal lifestyle choices and corporate innovation. This is a new best practice in the evolution of cities and real estate development, and a reflection of a deeply held value of Gale International. Indeed, as Anthony Townsend of the Institute for the Future has argued, ubiquitous computing will challenge urban design in the 21st century as much as the automobile did in the 20th century. This is the historic opportunity we are taking on with Songdo.

What is Songdo?

The Songdo vision begins first with its location. Songdo will reside on 1,500 acres of land reclaimed from the Yellow Sea on Incheon's waterfront. It is positioned as the "Gateway to Northeast Asia," a geographical hub just 40 miles southwest of Seoul and 25 miles from the North Korean Demilitarized Zone industrial area. This new urban center will be connected to the Incheon International Airport—one of the world's busiest—by a seven-mile highway bridge, and linked by subway to Seoul. Day travel is easy to China and Japan's major business centers. More than one-third of the world's population lives within a three-and-a-half-hour flying radius of Songdo.

Networked cities

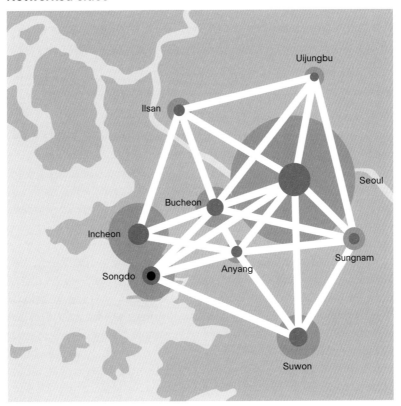

Figure 1 In the 1990s, the development of communication and information technologies boosted the growth of satellite cities in the greater Seoul region, establishing a networked, multicenter city structure in which each community has a commercial, cultural, and retail center of its own. Source: Kohn Pedersen Fox, 2006.

185

Songdo is a US$25 billion master-planned development on a scale unmatched worldwide. It is both a Korean national project and a unique international partnership, although one that remains essentially a private initiative. The owner of Songdo is New Songdo City Development, LLC, a 70:30 joint venture partnership between Gale International and Korean-based POSCO Engineering & Construction Co. Ltd., a subsidiary of the second largest steel company in the world. It represents the first project of its kind between a U.S. developer and a Korean company. Indeed, it is the first international real estate investment in South Korean history. Construction commenced in November 2004, and when completed in 2014, it is estimated that Songdo will be home to 65,000 residents and 300,000 commuters who will work there during the day.

Where the physical and virtual—and the public and the private—spheres meet will be a litmus test for other markets worldwide when it comes to the city's ubiquitous computing lifestyle.

Songdo will be the first "new" city in the world designed and planned as an international business district. It will include 50 million square feet of office space, 30 million square feet of residential space, 10 million square feet of retail space, 5 million square feet of hotel space, and 10 million square feet of public space, including a central park, neighborhood parks, a museum, an entertainment complex, schools, and an "Ecotarium," which will feature state-of-the-art "aquatecture" with fresh water and marine habitats.

Because of Songdo's central location within the Yellow Sea Economic Basin—which comprises an economically active population of more than 200 million with a gross domestic product (GDP) of US$1.3 trillion—it is positioned as the business hub for multinational companies in Northeast Asia. The South Korean Ministry of Trade and Finance expects the GDP of Northeast Asia—a region that includes northern China, eastern Russia, the Koreas, and Japan—to account for 30 percent of global GDP by 2020.

Corporations based in Songdo will enjoy the benefits of a Free Economic Zone—the first and largest in South Korea—designed to encourage direct foreign investment, operational efficiency, and relief from government bureaucracy. The Free Economic Zone will offer liberal tax incentives, exemption from mandatory hiring requirements, a U.S.-style legal system, and a foreign investment ombudsman office. Songdo will also sport a multinational currency and English as its primary language. And, foreigners can own land and run schools and hospitals.

Designed for synergy

A key principle of Songdo's design and planning, both in the physical and virtual sense, is deceptively simple: overlap. That is, where the physical neighborhoods of Songdo commingle is where the synergies of experience will occur. We fully expect that these neighborhoods will become the most interesting places to be. Similarly, where the physical and virtual—and the public and the private—spheres meet will be a litmus test for other markets worldwide when it comes to the city's ubiquitous computing lifestyle.

When it comes to planning, we closely considered neighborhood diversity and the mixture of buildings and densities. We don't want to build a city of discrete, isolated areas; nor do we want to attempt some kind of perfect order or rigid geometry. We mixed it up and condensed it all on 1,500 acres, which is the size of the central business district of Boston. In doing so, we had to convince local authorities that overlapping neighborhoods and usages are what create energy in a city. By and large, Korean zoning codes require distinct separation of building types by city blocks, and these blocks tend to be grouped together by districts. As much as possible, the Songdo plan brings different buildings and populations into close proximity. Our partner and master-plan architect, Kohn Pedersen Fox Associates PC, calls this "planned heterogeneity."

Architectural and aesthetic elements have been drawn from the world's greatest cities—for example, Venetian-style canals; a New York City-like Central Park; Parisian density; and Savannah, Georgia-inspired "pocket parks," small, outdoor areas open to the general public that are often of primarily environmental, rather than recreational, importance. Devoting 40 percent of Songdo to green space similarly was a foreign concept. Not only is that percentage much higher than in nearly any other Asian city, but the center of the city—its prime real estate—is devoted to parkland. Yet the elements borrowed from established cities are balanced by distinctly Korean features, such as residential "superblocks" set back from the street and the centrality of educational and cultural institutions.

While we integrated as much of the physical aspects of Songdo as we could, it seemed only natural that we should integrate technology in a similar fashion. We wanted public spaces that would bring people together and energize them—networked public spaces in which information will flow toward people, not just people flowing toward information.

Songdo's technology infrastructure is being afforded the same level of attention and significance as its roads, subways, sewers, and so on. Both residents and businesses will enjoy the benefits of a groundbreaking, ubiquitous computing environment, based on fixed-line fiber optics to every home and business; high-speed wireless computing access everywhere; fully integrated home networks; and the melding of facilities, IT, and property services under one operational and management structure. The latter functions will be controlled literally from one command center. Songdo will be among the first cities in the world to offer such an environment.

The business of U-Life

Through Songdo U-Life, LLC, our joint venture with leading Korean network integrator LG CNS Global, we will provide fully integrated property, facilities, and IT management services to residents and businesses. Since all information networks will be built from the ground up, there will be no redundant systems, thus keeping costs down and ensuring reasonable prices. Songdo U-Life plans to attract investors by forming a consortium mainly comprising service partners, while developing additional profit models throughout its operations.

A key differentiator of Songdo U-Life is that technology is viewed not just as necessary infrastructure, but as a profit generator. Technology companies will come to Songdo to develop new applications and business models that can be tested on a citywide or neighborhood basis and, if successful, exported elsewhere. Songdo offers an incredible opportunity to gauge the business value of proposed services *without providers having to build anything themselves*. For example, services that require widespread wireless data access or a common ID system can be implemented easily—a near impossibility in any other urban setting. Service partners will benefit greatly not only from a coherent and leading-edge technology infrastructure, but also from that infrastructure's integrated management. Songdo U-Life can provide a single organizational contact for all of the city's buildings, obviating the need for dealing with multiple building owners or associations.

Thus, the technology infrastructure will act as a profit center. Additionally, a portion of revenues will be invested in public projects benefiting the citizens of Songdo. We think many of the companies that use Songdo as a test bed will base their operations there, facilitating the development of a knowledge-based economic cluster similar to California's Silicon Valley. Significantly, South Korea's Ministry of Information and Communications has set aside US$297 million for companies setting up research facilities in Songdo in key IT growth areas, such as radio frequency identification (RFID) systems.

Businesses, organizations, government agencies, and individuals can create services built on Songdo's technology infrastructure. The possibilities range from the routine to the remarkable. For example, a resident's smart-card house key could be used to get on the subway, pay a parking meter, see a movie, or borrow a free public bicycle. The use of

U-City

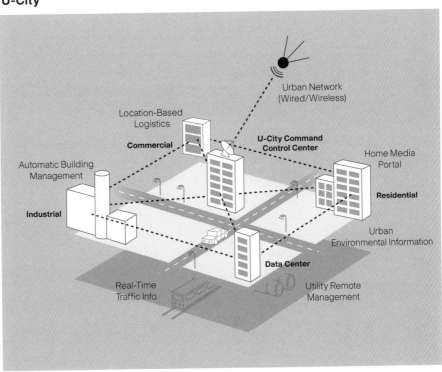

Figure 2 New Songdo City enables new technology without having to connect to existing buildings or legacy networks. For example, citywide wireless data access and a common ID system can be easily implemented. Source: Cisco, 2006.

189

a smart card is all that will be required for a quick jaunt across town in an electric smart car—there will be 10,000 such cars circulating in the city. Residents can take advantage of "one-click" billing to order services, such as pizza delivery or dry cleaning pickup, via the community portal or tenant-services portal (while also absolving the pizzeria and dry cleaner of having to build such functionality themselves).

Mobility is a crucial aspect of today's culture. In fact, the Korean government has established a national initiative to make wireless broadband accessible in all public areas of the country. In Songdo, the government-enabled IT infrastructure will tie in seamlessly with home networks so that residents will have access to their data from anywhere in the city. All content—photos, music, files, and more—will be unbound from home systems for use either on portable devices via wireless broadband or from a city kiosk or public screen.

It is important to note that privacy and data security are important priorities. Residents who do not want to make use of these services simply will not sign up for them. Everything will be based on a matter of choice.

Additionally, a ubiquitous data network makes the management of buildings much more efficient. Take something as mundane as a garbage can. If a garbage can is full, embedded sensors might automatically alert the facilities management team to empty it. Or public recycling bins could use RFID to credit recyclers every time they toss in a bottle.

The overall role of U-Life is that of a commerce facilitator, both for traditional and nontraditional usages, and of a community facilitator as well. The concept of unmonitored, shared resources—such as electric cars that can be borrowed and returned without the intervention of a human "monitor"—opens up fascinating possibilities. There is a strong community-building aspect in asking citizens to be responsible for shared city resources.

The promise of U-Culture

We would like to emphasize that Songdo U-Life is focused on ensuring that all the systems and services we implement are based on needs. LG CNS Global, our partner, helps us envision the possibilities while also understanding market demands, the technological challenges, and the preferences of Korean consumers. We want to channel users toward supportive technologies that will truly assist and improve their lives, not overwhelm them with gadgetry. We don't want to offer rich features at the cost of usefulness, which means we will need to educate consumers and help them make good choices.

The first wave of the Internet took place in front of a computer screen. Now we are in the second wave, where the power of the Internet becomes more infused in the physical world—in the built environment—and further permeates people's lives. To talk now in too detailed a way about specific applications is to miss the point of the possibilities inherent in a ubiquitous environment.

We like to use the analogy of the U.S. interstate highway system, a massive project in which tens of thousands of miles of roads were constructed with the stated goals of facilitating commerce and making the interior of the country more defensible. But that highway system also gave rise to something unexpected: a car culture that created entirely new and unexpected industries and, for better or worse, new ways of living in a more fast-paced, transient economy.

We want to channel users toward supportive technologies that will truly assist and improve their lives.

We expect that U-Culture will result in similarly unexpected applications, businesses, and ways of living. We plan to let our infrastructure and service offerings grow organically. Ubiquitous technologies should enable citizens to evolve with technology, and we have chosen to value such self-direction. Residents of Songdo need to experience the city on their own terms. So the key is to design for user needs, including those not yet identified, rather than designing around the technology. Songdo's success should be judged by the quality of the lives led by its inhabitants.

Our goal is for Songdo to embody a spirit of experimentation. And we believe that like all great cities, Songdo will be created by its citizens.

STANLEY C. GALE

CHAIRMAN, GALE INTERNATIONAL, UNITED STATES

Stanley Gale is a third-generation real estate entrepreneur. He founded The Gale Company in 1985 and led it to a position of prominence as one of the largest commercial development firms in the United States. A native of Long Island, New York, Gale holds a bachelor of arts degree from Rollins College and a master's degree in business administration from the Roy E. Crummer School of Business and Finance. He serves on the board of the Park Avenue Foundation and on the board of trustees for Drew University. Gale is a member of the Executive Committee of the U.S.-Korea Business Council.

Digital Images

1 **Aerial View**

New Songdo City boasts a variety of streets, buildings, zoning uses, open-space configurations, and landscape typologies, thereby creating myriad experiences for Songdo's visitors and residents.

Architect: Kohn Pedersen Fox Associates PC, 2006

APPENDIX

Selected Bibliography

Books

TRANSFORMING COMMUNITIES

Abramson, Bruce, *Digital Phoenix*, Cambridge, The MIT Press (2005)

Arup Global Foresight and Innovation Team, *Drivers Of Change 2006*, Barcelona, Editorial Gustavo Gili, SL (2006)

Austin, Robert D. and Bradley, Stephen P., *Broadband Explosion*, Boston, Harvard Business School Press (2005)

Burdett, Richard (Editor) and Ichioka, Sarah (Editor). *Cities: People, Society, Architecture: 10th International Architecture Exhibition*. Fondanzione La Biennale di Venezia. Rizolli, New York (2006)

Castells, Manuel, *The Information Age: Economy, Society and Culture, Volume 1:The Rise of the Network Society*, Oxford, Blackwell Publishing Ltd (2000)

Castells, Manuel, *The Information Age: Economy, Society and Culture, Volume 2: The Power of Identity*, Oxford, Blackwell Publishing Ltd (2000)

Castells, Manuel, *The Information Age: Economy, Society and Culture, Volume 3: End of Millenium*, Oxford, Blackwell Publishing Ltd (2000)

Dixon, Timothy; Thompson, Bob; McAllister, Patrick; Marston, Andrew and Snow, Jon, *Real Estate in the New Economy: The Impact of Information and Communications Technology*, Oxford, Blackwell Publishing Ltd (2005)

Dodge, Martin and Kitchin, Rob, *Mapping Cyberspace*, London, Routledge (2001)

Florida, Richard, *The Rise of the Creative Class: and How it's Transforming Work, Leisure, Community and Everyday Life*, New York, Basic Books (2002)

Florida, Richard, *The Flight of the Creative Class*, New York, HarperCollins (2005)

Forrester, Jay W., *Urban Dynamics*, Cambridge, MA, MIT Press (1969)

Forrester, Jay W., *World Dynamics*, Cambridge, MA, MIT Press (1971)

Gore, Al, *An Inconvenient Truth*, New York, Rodale (2006)

Horan, Thomas A., *Digital Places: Building Our City of Bits*, Washington, D.C., ULI-the Urban Land Institute (2000)

International Society of City and Regional Planners, *Making Spaces for the Creative Economy*, Madrid, ISoCaRP (2005)

Mau, Bruce and the Institute Without Boundaries, *Massive Change*, London, Phaidon Press (2004)

Mitchell, William J., *City of Bits: Space, Place, and the Infobahn*, Cambridge, The MIT Press (1995)

Mitchell, William J., *E-topia: Urban Life, Jim—But Not As We Know It*, Cambridge, The MIT Press (1999)

Mitchell, William J., *Me++: The Cyborg Self and the Networked City*, Cambridge, The MIT Press (2003)

Mitchell, William J.; Inouye, Alan S and Bluemnthal, Marjory S, *Beyond Productivity: Information Technology, Innovation and Creativity*, Washington, D.C., The National Academies Press (2003)

Mitchell, William J., *Placing Words: Symbols, Space, and the City*, Cambridge, The MIT Press (2005)

Sassen, Saskia, *Global Networks, Linked Cities*, New York, Routledge (2002)

TRANSFORMING WORKPLACES

Aardex Corporation, *User Effective Buildings*, Denver, Aardex Corporation (2004)

Allen, Tim; Bell, Adryan; Graham, Richard; Hardy, Bridget and Swafffer, Felicity, *Working Without Walls*, London, DEGW With The Office Of Government Commerce (2004)

Edwards, Victoria and Ellison, Louise, *Corporate Property Management: Aligning Real Estate with Business Strategy*, Oxford, Blackwell Publishing Ltd (2003)

Grech, Chris and Walters, David, *Future Office*, London, Taylor & Francis (2007)

Grosz, Andreas and Witt, Jochen, *Living At Work*, Munich, Hanser (2004)

Hascher, Rainer, *Office Buildings: A Design Manual*, Basel, Birkhaeuser (2002)

Malone, Thomas W, *The Future of Work: How the New Order of Business Will Shape Your Organization, Your Management Style, and Your Life*, Boston, Harvard Business School Press (2004)

NBBJ and Mau, Bruce, *Change Design: Conversations About Architecture as the Ultimate Business Tool*, Washington, D.C., Greenway Communications (2006)

Spath, Dieter and Kern, Peter, *Office 21: Push for the Future Better Performance of Working Environments*, Cologne, Egmont vgs Verlagsgesellschaft (2003)

Spencer, Nicholas C. and Winch, Graham M, *How Buildings Add Value For Clients*, London, Thomas Telford Publishing (2002)

TRANSFORMING BUILDINGS

ag4, *Media Facades*, Cologne, Daab (2006)

Buntrock, Dana, *Japanese Architecture As A Collaborative Process*, New York, Spon Press (2002)

Cohen, Jonathan, *Communication and Design With The Internet: A Guide For Architects, Planners and Building Professionals*, New York, W. W. Norton & Company (2000)

Gebäude Netzwerk Institut GNI, *GNI-Handbuch der Raumautomation: Gebäudetechnik mit Standardsystemen*, Berlin, VDE Verlag (1999)

Kieran, Stephen and Timberlake, James, *Refabricating Architecture: How Manufacturing Methodologies are Poised to Transform Building Construction*, New York, McGraw-Hill Professional (2003)

Kolarevic, Branko, *Architecture In The Digital Age: Design and Manufacturing*, New York, Spon Press (2003)

Liker, Jeffrey K., *The Toyota Way*, New York, McGraw-Hill (2004)

198

McDonough, William and Braungart, Michael, *Cradle To Cradle: Remaking the Way We Make Things*, New York, North Point Press (2002)

Womack, James P. and Jones, Daniel T, *Lean Thinking*, New York, Simon and Schuster (1996)

Yang, Jay; Brandon, Peter S. and Sidewell, Anthony C., *Smart & Sustainable Environments*, Oxford, Blackwell Publishing Ltd (2005)

Research reports available on websites

British Telecom. Society and Environment. A wide range of reports on the social, economic, and environmental impacts of technology. www.btplc.com/Societyandenvironment/Reports/Reports.htm

CoreNet Global, *Enabling Work in a Networked World: Intelligence on the Emerging Global Workplace*, www.corenetglobal.org/learning/core2010/index.vsp (2005)

Deutsche Bank Research, *e-Immobilien: Immobilienwirtschaft Im Internet Zeitalter*, www.dbresearch.de (2001)

Deutsche Bank Research, *Standortwahl in der vernetzten Welt – Kein Ende der Distanz*, www.dbresearch.de (2002)

Deutsche Bank Research, *Technik und Arbeit – Herausforderungen im 21. Jahrhundert*, www.dbresearch.de (2002)

Gartner & MIT, *The Agile Workplace: Supporting People and Their Work*, www.mit.edu/newsoffice/2002/agile-0403.html (2002)

I&I Limited, *IT Convergence In Buildings*, www.iandi.ltd.UK (2006)

Institute for Prospective Technological Studies (IPTS) / European Commission. *The future impact of ICT on the environment*, www.izt.de/sustainable_ict/projekte/future_impact_of_ict_on_env ironmental_sustainability.html (2004)

Intelligent Infrastructure Futures. Office of Science and Technology. www.foresight.gov.uk., London 2006

Intergovernmental Panel on Climate Change. *Climate Change 2007*. www.ipcc.ch

Johnson, Curtis and Walesh, Kim. *The New Global Fusion. Art, Technology and Community Development.* www.sjeconomy.com/publications/oedpubs.asp. San Jose, (2006)

Lean Constuction Institute Selected Readings—Extensive List, *Lean Construction, Production Controls, etc.,* Various Authors (1996 to Present) www.leanconstruction.org

National Institute Of Standards and Technology, *Cost Analysis of Inadequate Interoperability in the U.S. Capital Facilities Industry,* www.nist.gov, (2004)

The Sir John Egan Report, *Rethinking Construction,* www.constructingexcellence.org.uk/pdf/rethinking%20construc tion/rethinking_construction_report.pdf (1998)

Useful contacts for industry organizations, research, and education

TRANSFORMING COMMUNITIES

British Council for Offices (BCO)
BCO is Britain's leading forum for the discussion and debate of issues affecting the office sector. Its members are organizations involved in creating, acquiring, or occupying office space, whether architects, lawyers, surveyors, financial institutions, or public agencies. www.bco.org.uk

British Institute of Facility Management (BIFM)
BIFM is the U.K.'s lead institute representing the interests of those who practice facilities management and those who work in organizations supplying FM-related goods or services. www.bifm.org.uk

Facility Management Association (FMA) of Australia
FMA Australia represents professionals involved in the strategic and operational management of facilities in public and private sector organizations. www.fma.com.au

International Commercial and Corporate Real Estate Technology Resource (Realcomm)
Realcomm is an annual event and additional advisory services with the mission to provide a single place where industry leaders can come together to discuss, analyze, and debate the latest technology innovations that are impacting the commercial and corporate real estate industry. www.realcomm.com

Intelligent Community Forum (ICF)
The ICF is a not-for-profit think tank that focuses on job creation and economic development in the broadband economy. Its area of interest is the local community, both large and small, in developing and developed economies of the world. ICF conducts research, creates conference content, publishes information, and presents annual awards. www.intelligentcommunity.org

International Facility Management Association (IFMA)
IFMA is a member-centered association that exists to guide and develop facility management professionals. In support of its members, IFMA promotes the facility management profession by providing leadership, recognition, and standards of excellence. www.ifma.org

International Network of E-Communities (INEC)
Communities around the world are responding to the needs of their citizens by discovering new ways of using information and communication technologies for economic, social, and cultural development. Companies and governments that take advantage of these new technologies will create jobs and economic growth as well as improving the overall quality of life within the communities in which they take part. www.smartcommunity.nl

Japan Facility Management Promotion Association (JFMA)
JFMA represents professionals involved in the strategic and operational management of facilities in public and private sector organizations in Japan. www.jfma.or.jp

MuniWireless
MuniWireless is the portal for news and information about citywide wireless broadband projects around the world. These range from downtown hotzones to citywide and countywide wireless broadband networks. www.muniwireless.com

National Association of Building Owners and Managers (BOMA)
BOMA International is a primary source of information on office
building development, leasing, building operating costs, energy
consumption patterns, local and national building codes,
legislation, occupancy statistics, and technological developments.
www.boma.org

New Century Cities, MIT Center for Real Estate
New Century Cities is a joint research initiative from the Center
for Real Estate, City Design, and Development in Urban Studies
and Planning, and the Smart Cities Group/Media Lab. It focuses
on a new generation of development projects at the Massachusetts
Institute of Technology. www.mit.edu/CRE/research/ncc

Royal Institute of Chartered Surveyors (RICS)
The RICS is the leading source of land, property, construction,
and environmental knowledge in the U.K. It promotes best practices
and advises businesses, consumers, governments, and global
organizations. www.rics.org

SENSEable City Lab, MIT Media Lab
The increasing deployment of sensors and hand-held electronics
in recent years is allowing a new approach to the study of the built
environment. The way we describe and understand cities is being
radically transformed—alongside the tools we use to design them
and impact on their physical structure. Studying these changes
from a critical point of view and anticipating them is the goal of
the SENSEable City Laboratory, a new research initiative at the
Massachusetts Institute of Technology. www.senseable.mit.edu

Urban Land Institute (ULI)
ULI represents the entire spectrum of land use and real estate
development disciplines worldwide, working in private enterprise
and public service. The mission of the ULI is to provide responsible
leadership in the use of land to enhance the total environment.
www.uli.org

Frauenhofer Institut Arbeitswirtschaft und Organization—
Office 21
What will the office of the future look like? How will work be
organized? What information and communication processes will
take place? These are the questions asked by scientists at the
Fraunhofer Institute for Industrial Engineering IAO in Germany. To
answer them, Fraunhofer IAO has partnered with the office and real
estate industry to launch an innovation campaign: OFFICE 21.
www.office21.de

Future of Work
Future of Work is a membership organization for human resources,
IT, and facilities professionals who believe in the power and
importance of collective intelligence in creating the future. Its
focus is on the changing nature of work, the workforce, the
workplace, and management practices. www.thefutureofwork.net

Global Corporate Real Estate Organization (CoreNet Global)
CoreNet Global is the world's premier association for corporate real
estate and related professionals. www.corenetglobal.org

Global Research and Learning Network, Workplace Forum
Workplace Forum is a research and learning network focused
on global best practices in workplace design, technology, and
management. The forum aims to advance the understanding
and practice of the relationship between the evolving workplace
and business performance. www.workplaceforum.com

International Workplace Studies Program,
Cornell University (IWSP)
IWSP focuses on the ecology of new ways of working and is
an international leader in the study of Integrated Workplace
Strategies. Its research simultaneously considers the interplay
of work processes, physical design, information technology,
and organizational culture. www.iwsp.human.cornell.edu

International Workplace, Technology and Innovation Resource—
WorkTech
WorkTech is a U.K. conference dedicated to the impact of the
convergence of real estate and technology on the future of the
workplace. www.cordless.co.uk

American Institute of Architects (AIA)
The AIA is the voice of the architecture profession dedicated to serving its members, advancing their values, and improving the quality of the built environment. Through a culture of innovation, it empowers its members and inspires creation of a better built environment. www.aia.org

Center for Integrated Facilities Engineering,
Stanford University (CIFE)
The CIFE mission is to be the world's premier academic research center for Virtual Design and Construction of Architecture Engineering Construction industry projects. It aims to develop and test innovative new ways to model, visualize, analyze, and evaluate the multidisciplinary performance of design-construction projects, and to increase awareness of the value and costs of Virtual Design and Construction for practitioners. www.cife.stanford.edu

Computer Aided Architectural Design (CAAD), Swiss Federal
Institute of Technology ETH Zurich
The Chair for CAAD at ETH Zurich has an excellent international reputation and its goal is to develop CAAD as one of the best research centers for architecture and information, looking for new forms, structures, and processes for current architectural practice. www.wiki.arch.ethz.ch

Construction Industry Council (CIC)
CIC is the representative forum for the professional bodies, research organizations, and specialist business associations in the U.K. construction industry. www.cic.org.uk

Construction Industry Institute—The University of Texas
At Austin (CII)
CII is a consortium of leading owners, engineering and construction contractors, and suppliers who have a singular mission: to improve the cost effectiveness of the capital facility project lifecycle, from pre-project planning through completion and commissioning. www.construction-institute.org

Construction Users Roundtable (CURT)
CURT in the U.S. has a mission to create strategic advantage for construction users by providing aggressive leadership and focus on business issues that promote excellence in the development and execution of engineering, maintenance, and construction projects. www.curt.org

Design Intelligence
Design Intelligence is an international resource on the future of design; a repository of articles, original research, and industry news. It offers groundbreaking insight into future trends and management practices that will make any company a better managed and more financially successful business. www.di.net

ETHZ Swiss Federal Institute of Technology, Lausanne (EPFL)
The mission of the Media and Design Laboratory is to create a dynamic laboratory for the study and design of new media and digital technologies to enhance everyday environments and everyday life. It explores the vision of bringing physical and virtual environments together by designing, making, prototyping, and testing new interactive artifacts, objects, surfaces, and spaces. www.ldm.epfl.ch

Lean Construction Intitute (LCI)
LCI's purpose is to reform the management of production in design, engineering, and construction for capital facilities. LCI developed the Lean Project Delivery System (LPDS) that applies principles pioneered in manufacturing to construction. LPDS tools facilitate planning and control, maximizing value, and minimizing waste throughout the construction process. www.leanconstruction.org

Media Lab—MIT School of Architecture and Planning,
Massachusetts Institute of Technology
The Media Laboratory's vision of "enabling technology for learning and expression by people and machines" emphasizes technologies that improve the quality of life in the digital age. Its activity is focused on abstracting electronic content from its traditional physical representations, helping to create now-familiar areas such as digital video and multimedia. www.media.mit.edu

Royal Institute of British Architects (RIBA)
RIBA's mission is to advance architecture by demonstrating
benefit to society and promoting excellence in the profession.
It is a champion for architecture and for a better environment.
www.riba.org

ENVIRONMENTAL SUSTAINABILITY

Building Research Establishment (BRE)
BRE's Environmental Assessment Method (BREEAM) has
been used to assess the environmental performance of both new
and existing buildings in the U.K. It is regarded by Britain's
construction and property sectors as the measure of best practices
in environmental design and management.www.bre.co.uk

Center for Building Performance and Diagnostics,
Carnegie Mellon University (CBPD)
CBPD conducts research, demonstration, and teaching in
building performance and diagnostics. Its expertise ranges from
professional practice, to fundamental and applied research in
building physics, to advanced computer modeling and simulation
capabilities. www.arc.cmu.edu/cbpd

Energy Systems Laboratory, Texas A&M University (ESL)
ESL, established in 1939, is a division of the Texas Engineering
Experiment Station. Affiliated with the Department of Mechanical
Engineering and the College of Architecture, ESL develops and
transfers energy efficiency technology. www.esl.tamu.edu

The Ernest Orlando Lawrence Berkeley National Laboratory—
Building Technologies Department (Berkley Lab)
As a multi-program Department of Energy laboratory, Berkeley
Lab is dedicated to performing leading-edge research in the
biological, physical, materials, chemical, energy, environmental,
and computing sciences. www.btech.lbl.gov

U.S. Green Building Council (USGBC)—Leadership in Energy
and Environmental Design (LEED)
USGBC's core purpose is to transform the way buildings and
communities are designed, built, and operated, enabling an
environmentally and socially responsible, healthy, and prosperous
environment that improves the quality of life. www.usgbc.org

World Green Building Council (WorldGBC)
WorldGBC is the peak global not-for-profit organization working
to transform the property industry toward sustainability. It is
bringing together the Green Building Councils from around
the world to work together to share knowledge, resources,
and common principles to advance the development of greener
buildings. It also provides other countries wishing to start their
own Green Building Council with a diversity of solutions and
representation to ensure a successful start-up. www. worldgbc.org

DIGITAL BUILDING INFRASTRUCTURES

Asian Institute of Intelligent Buildings (AIIB)
AIIB's mission is to develop Asia's definition and standards for
Intelligent Buildings; to act as an independent certification
authority for Intelligent Buildings; to educate and promote the
community benefits of Intelligent Building; and to work with
international counterparts to bring Asia up to date on developments
in Intelligent Buildings. www.aiib.net

BuilConn
BuilConn is an event series that unites all the individuals involved in
buildings and IT in taking an objective and comprehensive view of
buildings and facilities, understanding the technologies and trends
that shape it, and discovering the steps required to implement truly
intelligent, integrated buildings. www.builconn.com

Building Industry Consulting Service International (BICSI)
BICSI is a professional association supporting the information
transport systems (ITS) industry with information, education, and
knowledge assessment for individuals and companies. ww.bicsi.org

Continental Automated Building Association (CABA)
CABA is a not-for-profit industry association that promotes
advanced technologies for the automation of homes and buildings
in North America. Its mission is to encourage the development,
promotion, pursuit, and understanding of integrated systems and
automation in homes and buildings. www.caba.org

Cybernetic Building System Program, Building and Fire Research Laboratory (BFRL)
The objective of the Cybernetic Buildings Program is to make available tested and demonstrated open Cybernetic Building Systems for improved productivity, lifecycle cost savings, energy conservation, improved occupant satisfaction, and market leadership. www.bfrl.nist.gov/goals_programs/prgmCBS

Harbor Research
Harbor Research is a research organization in the convergence of pervasive computing and global networking. The challenges and opportunities presented by the pervasive Internet are profound and go to the heart of how companies perceive the markets they are in, how they organize themselves, and how they approach business opportunities. www.harborresearch.com

Intelligent Building Group (IBG)
The IBG is an international association of leading professionals, from all sectors of the industry, looking to increase contacts, share knowledge, and propose solutions for the sustainable advancement of the built environment. www.ibgroup.org.uk

Swiss Building Networks Institute (GNI)
GNI is a professional association supporting the building technology industry with information, education, and knowledge assessment for individuals and companies. www.g-n-i.ch

INTEROPERABILITY & DATA STANDARDS

Computer Integrated Building Processes Group,
The National Institute of Standards and Technology (CIBP)
CIBP reduces the cost and improves the quality of facility engineering, construction, and operation processes by developing and testing open standards for the representation, exchange, and sharing of information throughout the facility lifecycle. The current focus of the group is on the use of open information standards in collaborative processes. www.cic.nist.gov

International Alliance of Interoperability (IAI)
IAI is a global standards-setting organization representing
widely diverse constituencies—from architects and engineers, to
research scientists, to commercial building owners and contractors,
to government officials and academia, to facility managers, to
software companies, and to building product manufacturers.
Alliance members are committed to promoting effective means
of exchanging information among all software platforms and
applications serving the AEC+FM community by adopting a
single Building Information Model. www.iai-na.org

Open Building Information Xchange (oBIX)
The purpose of oBIX is to define a standard Web services
protocol to enable communications between building mechanical
and electrical systems and enterprise applications. This protocol
will enable facilities and their operations to be managed as full
participants in knowledge-based businesses. oBIX is currently a
Technical Committee of the Organization for the Advancement of
Structured Information Standards, a not-for-profit, international
consortium that drives the development, convergence, and
adoption of e-business standards. www.obix.org

Open Standards Consortium for Real Estate (OSCRE)
OSCRE's mission is the development, synthesis, and adoption of
e-business standards that enable the real estate industry to function
effectively and efficiently in the new economy. OSCRE enables the
electronic transfer of information directly from one system into
another and removes the need to send hard copy or to re-enter data
manually. www.oscre.org

Acknowledgements

Connected Real Estate is a creative and collaborative effort of stakeholders from both the Cisco Internet Business Solutions Group (IBSG) and the Cisco Worldwide Real Estate and Workplace Resources Group (WPR). The editors would like to extend their thanks to everyone for their teamwork and cooperation in making this book a reality:

Cisco
EXECUTIVE SPONSORS
Gary Bridge, Toby Burton, Mark Golan, Christina S. Kite

INTERNET BUSINESS SOLUTIONS GROUP
Ron Biggs, Cynthia Bournellis, Kathy Burrows, Bryan Culp, Lisa Daniels, Damien Dunne, Robert Moriarty, Maria-José Sobrini, Herb Wang, Kay Watanabe, Eric Wee

WORLDWIDE REAL ESTATE AND WORKPLACE RESOURCES GROUP
Martin Bauer, Julie Garden, Vic Ortiz, Robert Thurman

CONNECTED REAL ESTATE COMMUNITY OF INTEREST
Sam Alkharrat, Thomas Arnold, Dave Clute, Alexander Heimbach, Rick Huijbregts, Ray Rapuano, Amr Salem, Nabil Shamaa, Barbara Sullivan, Jim Walsh

Authors
ARUP
Olivia Gadd, Ben Richardson

BANK OF AMERICA
Tom Doran, Ferrell Jones, Lynn Rieger

CARNEGIE MELLON UNIVERSITY
Chas di Fatta

DEGW
Gabriel Hobbs

GALE COMPANY
Mary Lou DiNardo, John Hynes, Pamela O'Connell, Carl Seaholm

HOCHTIEF/TURNER
Wolfgang Katzer, Doug Nies, Frank Schroeder, Dirk Steffen

MIT
Michael Joroff

REGUS
Paula Knight

SUNTEC CITY
Kenny Wong

ZARAGOZA
Ricardo Avero

Other

TRUSTED ADVISORS
Andrew Armstrong, Leslie Erganian, Richard Hodges,
Patrick Nielsen, Gail Otteson, Christine Ross, Bruno Schindler,
Danny Seaton, Andrew Thomson

PUBLISHER
Lesley Daley

WRITERS
Manek Dubash, Keith Rodgers

DESIGNERS
Stephen Kirk, Chris Wright

The Connected Series
Thought-provoking essays
from industry leaders

A series of books covering top-of-mind issues across a range of public and private industry sectors.

Each book presents a Cisco perspective on the sector, and includes a range of essays from many of the world's leading CXOs, innovators, and visionaries.

Order online at
www.cisco.com/go/connectedseries

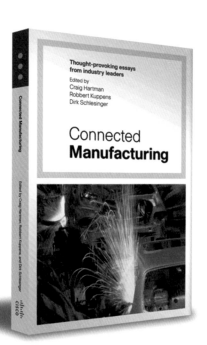

New Title
Connected Manufacturing
Edited by Craig Hartman, Robbert Kuppens, and Dirk Schlesinger

Manufacturing industries face unprecedented challenges. New competitors are emerging from countries such as China and India; incumbent companies are beginning to reap benefits from global supply chains; and customers are demanding customized products. To survive, manufacturers must reduce costs by standardizing processes and products globally, while responding flexibly to the needs of customers regionally.

ISBN 0-9550411-4-7   160 x 240mm   144 pages

Connected Cities

Edited by Simon Willis

The ideas explored in *Connected Cities* chart the emergence of a political and economic phenomenon—the city as the connected republic of the 21st century. Simon Willis, global head of e-government for the Cisco Internet Business Solutions Group, has collected essays that show how different cities are grappling with the various stages of connectivity.

ISBN 0-9546445-1-4   160 x 240mm   116 pages

Connected Health

Edited by Kevin Dean

Healthcare is consistently debated and is the highest priority on the agenda of citizens, public servants, and nations. The advent of the Internet and communication technologies is changing the way we provide care. This collection of essays stretches the intellect and highlights the drivers for changing the way information is used to deliver better, faster, and lower-cost healthcare using real-world experience.

ISBN 0-9546445-0-6   160 x 240mm   116 pages

Connected Schools

Edited by Michelle Selinger

We live in a knowledge society, where connectivity delivers information at unprecedented speeds and in multiple formats, and creates opportunities for new partnerships. In this exciting age, education is the prime driver for economic growth, peace, and prosperity. *Connected Schools* demonstrates how governments across the world are realizing the need to focus resources on the evolution of their educational systems, and how they are using new technology and the Internet to drive change.

ISBN 0-9546445-5-7   160 x 240mm   168 pages

Connected Homes

Edited by Fernando Gil de Bernabé y Varela

The communications industry is undergoing massive change, and nowhere is this more evident than in the arena of consumer broadband. Virtually every service provider is attempting to capture this still-nascent but exploding market—from incumbents, alternative service providers, and cable and satellite operators to mobile and Internet portals. This selection of essays provides a look at the forces that are shaping the consumer broadband market, with the goal of helping service providers adapt to and profit from this opportunity.

ISBN 0-9546445-6-5   160 x 240mm   152 pages

Connected Government

Edited by Willi Kaczorowski

Connected Government consists of 14 essays from leaders in national governments, outlines the concept of a connected government, and examines the issues involved in developing and implementing compelling, national e-government strategies. It explores the connected government strategy, which is built on six pillars: citizen centricity, standardized common infrastructure, back-office reorganization, governance, new organizational models, and social inclusion.

ISBN 0-9546445-8-1   160 x 240mm   152 pages

Connected Workforce

Edited by Simon Aspinall and Anja Jacquin Langer

Mobility has been critical to human survival since the beginning of history. The collection of essays in *Connected Workforce* brings together the views of senior business leaders and renowned market innovators on how mobility is changing their business practices and shaping our future.

ISBN 0-9546445-9-X   160 x 240mm   144 pages

Connected Transportation

Edited by Pravin Raj, Syed Hoda, and Howard Lock

In *Connected Transportation*, the editors bring together perspectives from industry CEOs, senior business executives, authorities, and visionaries from a wide range of segments of the transportation industry. These essays explore the current state of the industry, viable strategies for meeting its challenges, and opportunities that lie ahead.

ISBN 0-9551959-0-X   160 x 240mm   144 pages

Order online at www.cisco.com/go/connectedseries

Connected Cities

Connected Schools

Connected Homes

Connected Government

Edited by Simon Willis

Edited by Michelle Selinger

Edited by Fernando Gil de Bernabé y Varela

Edited by Willi Kaczorowski

Connected

Essays from innovators

Cisco Systems

Design: Loman Street Studio
www.lomanstreetstudio.com

Printed by G&B Printers.
Telephone +44 (0)20 8755 1822